*3,ᴴ

Parkman's History

YALE HISTORICAL PUBLICATIONS

LEWIS P. CURTIS · EDITOR

PUBLISHED UNDER THE DIRECTION OF

THE DEPARTMENT OF HISTORY

FROM THE INCOME OF

THE FREDERICK JOHN KINGSBURY

MEMORIAL FUND

GEOFFREY CUMBERLEGE, OXFORD UNIVERSITY PRESS

LONDON

OTIS A. PEASE

PARKMAN'S HISTORY

THE HISTORIAN AS LITERARY ARTIST

YALE UNIVERSITY PRESS

NEW HAVEN 1953

FOR WALDO

*Chief among these motives was the overwhelming idea
of the great whale himself. Such a portentous and
mysterious monster roused all my curiosity. Then
the wild and distant seas where he rolled his island
bulk; the undeliverable nameless perils of the whale;
these, with all the attending marvels of a thousand
Patagonian sights and sounds, helped to sway me to
my wish. With other men, perhaps, such things
would not have been inducements; but as for me, I
am tormented with an everlasting itch for things
remote. I love to sail forbidden seas and land on
barbarous coasts. Not ignoring what is good, I am
quick to perceive a horror, and could still be
social with it—would they let me—since it is but
well to be on friendly terms with all the inmates
of the place one lodges in.*

—MOBY DICK, *chap. 1.*

Introduction

HISTORY written from recorded documents is necessarily at two removes from the actual event. That is not to say that the recorded documents are therefore "closer" to the actuality. Between the fact-as-event and the fact-as-record the curtain has fallen forever. The documents, it is true, are often the only facts which remain, and pure history in a strict sense can only duplicate the document. But fortunately there exists more than pure history. One may depend upon continuity of experience. The historian who reads the document brings to his reading a consciousness of his own experience. He may recognize in the document data which correspond to the data of his own consciousness. The more extensive his own experiences are, the more he is apt to recognize in the record. What the document reveals and what his own experience reveals may be so consistent with each other that he may eventually begin to enlarge on the document, to supply with his experience the missing details. If he is a good historian his rendering of the document and of what he sees behind the document will result in history that is closer than the document to the actuality of events and to the experience of his readers. He has re-created the event.

For what purpose? Is it because the historian is obsessed with the compulsion to present truth or to further scientific knowledge? Either way, he must recognize that he does not present truth; he merely re-creates out of the materials at hand and out of his own experience a new *version* of the truth, and if he creates well his version may stand unimpaired by the discovery of new evidence in the future. What criteria determine how he constructs his version of truth? In addition

to the obvious criteria of historical research and the evaluation
of evidence the historian has practically an infinite number to
choose from.

I propose in this essay to describe and analyze Francis
Parkman's version of the truth, his re-creation of the events of
history. More has been written about Parkman the man than
about his works, and, while few historians have ever been
more worthy of biography, I would prefer ultimately to come
to grips with the works and not the man. Consequently I have
tried to hold the "external biography" (Perry Miller's phrase)
to a minimum, a biography gleaned mainly from Mason
Wade's studies and from his edition of the Parkman Journals.
I shall first discuss Parkman's early work and literary development as a preliminary phase to his major seven-volume history
of New France, and an important phase in view of the surpris-
ing consistency of interest and purpose which linked his earliest writings with his last. I shall then attempt to examine the
principal elements in his major works in order to see what he
did with history and how he combined literary artistry with
fact to the enrichment of both, which in a sense was his significant achievement. Despite the number of studies devoted
to Parkman's life and his techniques as a historian, few attempts have been made to investigate analytically and carefully either his literary style or the significance of his structure
of history. I feel that it is equally important to discover why
Parkman's writing has endured longer than that of his contemporaries among historians and where he stands in relation
to them.

In addition to the two works by Mason Wade, *Francis Parkman, Heroic Historian* (New York, 1942), and *The Journals
of Francis Parkman* (2 vols., New York, 1947), I am indebted
to a few of the Parkman Papers in the Massachusetts Historical Society in Boston and in the Harvard University Library
in Cambridge. Other works consulted include C. H. Farnham,
A Life of Francis Parkman (Boston, 1900), W. L. Schramm,

Francis Parkman, Representative Selections (New York, 1938), and Eric F. Goldman, "The Historians," in *A Literary History of the United States* (New York, 1948). Parkman's writings remain the principal source for this study. For his seven books on "France and England in North America" I have used throughout the Frontenac edition (15 vols. Boston, 1903), which includes Parkman's final revisions. His other writings I have cited in full.

I must make explicit at least one assumption governing this study. Unless I specifically indicate to the contrary I have not seen fit to call into question Parkman's historical accuracy or his statements of fact. Historians have universally agreed that he took great pains with his facts and that in his day he was the best documented writer in his field. He has been accused of minor errors, and he had some distinct prejudices. But such points are incidental to this study. My concern is to determine how Parkman was able to achieve such vivid effects from his facts.

Many people have made this present book possible. I cite them here with fervent thanks for help and encouragement freely given: as teachers and advisors, Leonard W. Labaree, David M. Potter, George W. Pierson, and Samuel F. Bemis; as editor of the Wallace Notestein Essays, Lewis P. Curtis, for his unfailing patience and careful standards of craftsmanship and style; and finally Edward Haynes and my wife, Mary, for the discussions, suggestions, criticisms, and inspiration which eventually produce books and even authors.

OTIS A. PEASE

New Haven, Conn., 1953

Contents

CHAPTER ONE

Preparation

*All history becomes subjective; in other words
there is properly no history, only biography.
Every mind must know the whole lesson for itself—
must go over the whole ground. What it does not
see, what it does not live, it will not know.*
      —RALPH WALDO EMERSON, "History," *Essays:
      First Series*

SOMETIME before the early months of 1842, Francis Parkman,
an eighteen-year-old sophomore at Harvard College, had
determined for himself a program of work which was to claim
his lifelong energies. In his later years, at least, he viewed himself as having had a fixed and consistent purpose. He wrote that,
when still at Harvard, "my various schemes had crystallized
into a plan of writing a story of what was then known as the
'Old French War' . . . for here, as it seemed to me, the forest
drama was more stirring and the forest stage more thronged
with appropriate actors than in any other passage of our history. . . ." [1] In another letter, written in 1864 and referring to
himself in the third person, he declared that his ambition had
been set for literary and historical writing and that he had
subsequently molded his life to it. "The reliance was less on
books than on such personal experiences as should, in some

1. Letter to Martin Brimmer, 1886, quoted in Mason Wade, ed.,
The Journals of Francis Parkman (New York, Harper and Bros.,
1947), p. xi. Hereafter cited as Wade, *Journals*.

1

sense, identify him with his theme. His natural inclinations urged him in the same direction." He added that his boyhood fancy had been "a life of action and a death in battle"; his present illness was irksome to him in that, amid a Civil War, he was forced to "live in the past, not the present, and wield a pen, not a sword." [2]

The romanticism implicit in his early enthusiasm for camping in the wilderness and absorbing the "forest drama" of Indian life was supported and reinforced by the documented accounts of pioneer exploits and adventure. Thus he found two kinds of "reality"—personally verifiable experiences and the documented facts of the experiences of others. Could he not express each in terms of the other? Could he not reconcile the literary expression of his youthful "natural inclinations" for the "life of action" with the historical expression of what actually happened? The one would include the heroic exploit, the rendering of vigorous characters who battled against adversity and danger; the other had to be truthful, to the extent that it "happened." Beyond that there were no limits to the subject matter of historical writing, but current tradition from Gibbon to Prescott approved of cosmic drama about cultural forces and civilized or barbarous nations, a drama that told a story and pointed a moral. In the ten years that followed the "crystallized" plan of his sophomore year Parkman succeeded in formulating his fundamental approach to his work and to the problems of history itself. By 1851 he had developed the fully elaborated theme which is so carefully outlined in the opening chapters of *The Conspiracy of Pontiac* and which, with some exceptions noted below, was to remain generally unaltered through the entire series as a structure for his history.

Parkman's first public attempts at expressing his theme suggest clearly that the roots of his literary interests were as much

2. Letter to Dr. Ellis, 1864, from original copy in the Francis Parkman Papers, Massachusetts Historical Society.

personal and romantic as historical. In 1845 the *Knickerbocker* carried three short adventure tales and a narrative poem, two anonymous and two under the pseudonym of Capt. Jonathan Carver, Jr. They deserve close scrutiny; in one form or another they mark Parkman's apprenticeship in style and craft, and they demonstrate especially the way in which he interwove personal experience with historical structure to gain a sense of immediacy. The first to appear was "The Ranger's Adventure," a four-page frontier "tall tale" of a young doctor who joins a band of Roger's Rangers at Lake George in the winter of 1755.[3] The band of rangers met a war party of Indians who surprised and killed every ranger in the band but the doctor. Fleeing through the snow-wrapped forest this lone survivor wheeled around and fired at the first pursuing savage, who was running so fast that when he fell his "shaven head ploughed up the snow for yards." A second savage was impaled through his chest on a pine bough over which the doctor had leaped. The doctor escaped to live to a ripe old age and told the tale to "me" who heard it "a few years ago." Despite some strained devices and uneven narration, the tale was written clearly and vividly with short sentences and vigorous verbs. Parkman seems to have been bothered by the problem of how to work into the story the description—from his own experience—of snow on the boughs of trees and a word picture of the forest, but he evoked the scene more successfully than he did the action, the details of which seem to display horror and brutality for their own sake and obviously did not come from Parkman's own experience.

The second and much the best tale is really two stories in one. Entitled "The Scalp-Hunter," it opens with Parkman's apparently faithful rendering of an actual occurrence in the New Hampshire wilderness in 1724, when a party of eight settlers tracked eleven Indian marauders into the White Mountain re-

3. *The Knickerbocker*, 25 (March 1845), 198 ff.

gion.[4] Night fell, the settlers surrounded and surprised the Indians and slaughtered all but one. The narrator identifies himself with the pursuing party, and from this stems his strength
of prose, even though he actually views and relates the incident
only as a remote chronicler of events. The descriptions of the
forest and its color are firsthand, and seem to make real a savage
wilderness into which scarcely less savage men are penetrating.
Allowing one Indian to escape then enabled Parkman to graft
onto his historical narrative a fictional man hunt that was
plainly a projection of one of his own youthful adventures into
a realm of exploit and danger which, after his physical afflictions
in 1846, were destined to exist for him only in his imagination.
While the rest of the party turned back, one member followed
on in solitary pursuit of the Indian. The pursuer's trek through
tangled fallen growth, over streams and up gorges into the heart
of Crawford Notch, came straight from Parkman's own experience. An often-quoted passage from Parkman's Journal of 1841
describes his rather foolhardy climb up the face of the avalanche
behind the Willey House in the Notch.[5] Ascending to a point
where a sheer rock wall barred the way up and crumbling, loose
rocks made descent impossible, Parkman inched his way across
to the edge of the slide, using his jackknife as a piton. He barely
reached the edge, and a log which he sent crashing and bound-
ing down several hundred feet revealed to him the fate that was
nearly his. Parkman avails himself of this passage from his
Journal for the climax of his Indian tale. The pursued savage
dashed up the avalanche path to the cliff wall and, as Parkman
did, gained the forest above. The hunter reached the cliff but
was unable to follow; his rifle fell and shattered on the rocks far
below. Trapped on the edge the hunter survived two days,
when he lost his perch in a rainstorm and plunged to his death.
The hunted Indian scalped the hunter and survived "to tell the
tale."

4. *The Knickerbocker*, 25 (April 1845), 297 ff.
5. See Wade, *Journals*, pp. 13–14.

Such a tale was more than a mere re-creation of personal experience: it symbolized Parkman's conscious concern for heroic adventure, represented in a figurative and actual quest for the Indian and an artistically valid transfer of identity related to the ironic implications of the title. The hunter possessed in germinal form the traits which Parkman was to stress again and again in his heroes—tenacity of purpose and unflinching courage in the face of hostile forces, whether of nature or of man. Here one also notices Parkman's earliest method of establishing his theme and its sense of immediacy for the reader. Using actual experience, intrinsically valuable, he remade the situation and environment to suit the artistic needs of the story. Promising as is this example of Parkman's craftmanship, it also indicates where his real gifts lay. The factual material of the action (and action was the basic ingredient of Parkman's entire writing) had to be supplied him directly, either from his own experience or from documents. Whenever Parkman relied on his imagination to supply action, he usually failed to communicate it to his readers, a failure nowhere more evident than in "Satan and Dr. Carver," the third tale of this series.[6] Its elaborate plot echoed the contemporary bathos of the "annual" and would have been ludicrous even for Cooper, whom Parkman might well have been imitating. Despite his penchant for the romantic he had to rely on the solidity of observable fact or recorded history.

Another contribution, "The New Hampshire Ranger," shows what might have happened had he restricted his poetic style to verse form.[7] By this time he could handle descriptive passages with assurance, and his language possessed a directness and vigor shared by few of his contemporaries. Some of his imagery foreshadows the most effective word pictures of his later years. One feels the sultry August heat in the languor of a frontier valley, or sees the crisp scarlet-brown of the Adirondacks in October. But the florid idiom and unvaried meter betray a lack

6. *The Knickerbocker, 26* (December 1845), 515 ff.
7. *Ibid., 26* (August 1845), 146–7.

of poetic talent which, happily for historians, Parkman never chose to remedy. This brief excursion into poetry merely allowed him to reminisce subjectively and fictionally: I was a ranger, and my life was glorious.

For Parkman the ranger the years through 1846 provided a basis for firsthand research attained by few historians before or since. The "Old French Wars," let alone their predecessors, had never been adequately examined. He had not only to blaze and clear his own trail through unexplored history; he had to determine the very substance and scope of that history. Few if any in America were better favored by environment to succeed. Boston was the only important American center of historical materials, and Jared Sparks, his early adviser, knew both the value of foreign archives and how to start a young firebrand upon his investigations.[8] The prodigious task of collecting documents was scarcely greater than finding them or copying them, but Parkman was financially able to see the project through to completion. Perhaps it was only right that the fortune gathered by his merchant grandfather soon after the end of the English-French rivalry in North America should be expended on the history of that very rivalry. Furthermore, Parkman's reading and his formal studies were of the best. He was not sufficiently attracted by the study of law to make it a career, but his training in law may well have helped him to analyze the materials of history. His tour of Europe, though it seems to have had little influence on his writing, undoubtedly stimulated his awareness of the cultural differences between the only society he had known, one of Anglo-Saxon derivation, and the older Catholic-oriented societies, inheritors of the tradition that had molded French Canada. He was beginning to establish his lifelong contacts with archivists, historians, antiquarians, and ethnologists, who helped him build up a source collection of unprecedented excellence. It is equally true that beyond his circle of friends

8. For a discussion of Parkman's exceptional position for historical study, see Wade, *Journals,* pp. xiv–xv.

Parkman shunned almost every current of American life that lacked relevance to the re-creation of an age dead for a century when he began to study it. Before he could imbue the past with the life of his present experience he had to give himself completely to the past.

Parkman's summer trips into the semiwilderness that still clung to the worn-down stubs of New England mountains both fulfilled and whetted his craving for the solitary hardihood of the romantic-heroic hunter. He was also storing away the experience of border settlers, trappers, and explorers whose lives had been molded by the all-coercive presence of the forest. His knowledge of forest life would later serve as a point of contact between the lost environment and the reader. Another element in his scheme, the Indian and his culture, Parkman had still to absorb directly; in 1846 the chance was offered. He journeyed to the Laramie Mountains and lived for several weeks in a tribe of the Plains Sioux. He wrote of his trip in his journal and in a classic, though watered-down, tale of travel; but a more important result was his opportunity to acquire a personal knowledge of the behavior and the surface realities of the Indian. In one way or another this experience served him throughout the rest of his life.

Although *The Oregon Trail* might without exaggeration be analyzed as a contribution to history in its own right, it can be considered more significantly as a final preparation for the writing of full-scale history. The problem of reconciling immediacy with documentary reality was still in the future, for *The Oregon Trail* consisted only in the immediacy. Yet, despite revisions and "editing" by Charles Eliot Norton and others,[9] the writing anticipated the subtleties and complexities of Parkman's later work; by this time he was able and ready to express his knowledge of an alien culture and at least a suggestion of its patterns of behavior. Perhaps the foremost quality of his "Oregon" story

9. See Wade, *Journals*, pp. 385–7.

is its ability to evoke an awareness of the raw new land, its
weather, and its moods. The impact is as direct on the reader
as it was on Parkman. Formal rhetorical devices frequently
dilute his style; one seeks in vain the penetrating, terse exactness
of his later writing; yet the descriptions are related functionally
to the men who experienced them and are therefore integrated
into the narrative with a success that Parkman had less chance
to repeat later when confronted with multiple problems in re-
creating the experiences of others.

In telling of an experience in a rainstorm on a Kansas prairie,
for example, the most convincing passages describe not the
immensities of sky and land but the observed actions of men and
the small-scale drama of a rain-soaked tent:

> Not a breath of air. . . . The sun beat down upon us with
> a sultry and penetrating heat almost insupportable, and as
> our party crept slowly along over the interminable level,
> the horses hung their heads as they waded through the mud,
> and the men slouched into the easiest position upon the
> saddle. At last, towards evening, the old familiar black heads
> of thunder-clouds rose fast above the horizon. . . . A cool
> wind, filled with the smell of rain, just then overtook us,
> levelling the tall grass by the side of the path. . . . It came
> upon us almost with the darkness of night; the trees, which
> were close at hand, were completely shrouded by the roaring
> torrents of rain. . . .
>
> Our tent was none of the best. . . . The rain beat through
> the canvas in a fine drizzle. . . . We sat upon our saddles
> with faces of the utmost surliness, while the water dripped
> from the visors of our caps, and trickled down our cheeks.[10]

10. *The Oregon Trail*, pp. 56–8. Citations are to the first edition,
*The California and Oregon Trail: being sketches of prairie and Rocky
mountain life* (New York, G. P. Putnam, 1849). This was a revision
of the initial serial publication in *The Knickerbocker*, Vols. *29–33*
February 1847–February 1849). Later revisions in 1872 and 1892.
The passage quoted was unchanged in all revisions.

Much of Parkman's ability to convey the reality of the plainsmen was based on emphasizing the relation of men to weather or to land. He appealed to the reader's own experience of nature, its violence for example, and so enabled him to sense the moods of the men in the story. The narrator does not say what the men felt or thought. Every word conveys only what an observer saw: the "faces," not the "men," were surly. Parkman displayed here what he was to achieve repeatedly in his histories, though not always so successfully: a detached, accurate objectivity which anticipated the techniques of later naturalistic fiction and journalism, together with a complementary ability to involve the reader in the action and mood of a historical event.

Foreshadowed in *The Oregon Trail* was the heroic type of character to be found in his histories. Henry Chatillon in life had been real enough and doubtless heroic enough for Parkman's purposes. But as a hero Parkman created him larger than life and seemed content merely to pin labels on him rather than present him through action or conflict. For example: "His manly face was the mirror of uprightness, simplicity, and kindness of heart. . . . He was a proof of what unaided nature will sometimes do." [11] Such romantic preconceptions, to say nothing of the rhetoric, seldom crept into Parkman's histories (or when they did they seldom interfered with the history) for the simple reason that he knew better than to tamper with history. He significantly was less able to re-create men whom he knew personally than those who lived for him only in their records. One may be thankful that he was not able to know La Salle and Frontenac in person; what ex cathedra moral judgments might have followed!

Parkman's familiarity with Indian life as revealed in *The Oregon Trail* was of great value for his later work. However inadequate by ethnological standards, his descriptions were virtually the first to combine realism and intelligent reporting with literary art. His Indians may not think or speculate, but

11. *Ibid.*, pp. 22–3.

they ride and hunt and otherwise behave for the reader very
much as white men must have seen them do for three centuries.
Wade points out that Parkman did not rely on observations
alone; he had in Henry Chatillon and Tom Fitzpatrick two excellent firsthand sources for his insight into Indian culture.[12]
As his histories progressed Parkman was to rely more and more
on subsequent published research and observation. He was
careful to utilize his own experiences only for added details of
mood and atmosphere and behavior clearly consistent with the
documents themselves and implicit in them.

The first product of Parkman's initial impulse to write history
was appropriately a transitional work. *The Conspiracy of
Pontiac* is in a formal sense a part of his unified conception, but
in terms of what he eventually made of his later history one
might better consider it a summary to his preliminary studies.
He completed it slowly and under great difficulty soon after
The Oregon Trail appeared. In the preface Parkman said that
the book "aims to portray the American forest and the
American Indian at the period when both received their
final doom." [13] It was to show how the French colonial forces,
having befriended the Indian and so delayed his destruction,
were finally driven from the continent by English settlers whose
interests were incompatible with the Indian. The defeat of his
French allies confirmed the Indian's fate and that of the forest
he lived in. The nature of his culture made it impossible for
him to survive without the wilderness or to organize an effective
political or military opposition to English colonial expansion.
Pontiac came closest to achieving an intertribal alliance, but
the weaknesses of the Indian character proved his undoing. His
initial successes owed less to savage virtues than to slow-moving
colonial administrations.

12. Wade, *Journals*, p. 394.
13. *The Conspiracy of Pontiac* (Frontenac ed., Boston, Little,
Brown and Co., 1903), *1*, x. Hereafter cited as *Pontiac*.

The first four chapters of *Pontiac,* commonly considered to
provide an accurate summary of Parkman's work, do so only in
a superficial sense. They trace the rivalry of the French and
English over a century and a half solely in terms of their differing relations to the American forest and the Indian. Though
Parkman labeled New France absolutist and New England
democratic, though one he described as fed "artificially" from
overseas, the other as self-supporting, he did not then attach to
this contrast the importance it had for him later, when he interpreted the opposing systems as a product of European maritime rivalry. The theme outlined in *Pontiac* in some measure
foreshadows the theme of the later series, but in some ways it
differs significantly and is notably less complex. It suggests, for
example, that the two colonial forces inevitably came to dispute
the possession and disposal of the American wilderness lands
and their inhabitants. The French depended on the fur trade
and believed in saving Indian souls through the church. The
English cut down the forest and tended to regard the Indians as
incapable of salvation. When the two powers clashed they
clashed in a wilderness war, fought by Indians, French, and
English on the terms of the forest, not of Europe. Such an interpretation plainly underlay Parkman's early interest in the active
life of rangers and in the pageantry and color of the Old French
War. In *Pontiac* Parkman gave little attention to the economic
and institutional rivalries of the English and French nations or
to the long string of conflicts that were European in origin and
which could not be explained primarily in colonial terms.
Equally limited in scope was Parkman's summary of Indian culture. In *Pontiac* it provides merely a background of detail help-
ful for the description of the uprising. When later he came to
write of the Jesuit missions, he was obliged to rewrite the
Indian chapter, not just to include newer information but to account for a different set of circumstances in an earlier century.
The dramatic interest in *Pontiac* depends on the single large-
scale conflict of Indians with the English colonists and troops,

while the remaining histories consider the Indians in a far more complex relation: the interaction between Indians, priests, traders, soldiers, and settlers, both French and English, over a century and a half.

Pontiac, in short, is less a sequel to the finished history than a unified treatment of a subject only partially related to the end product and with somewhat different premises. Its subject tends to reflect Parkman's youthful concept of what he wished most to find in the historical record. The action rages a little more fiercely, the warfare seems more bloody and savage, and the warriors more dashing and statuesque than what Parkman's later perspective and devotion to the thematic structure permitted. One heroic exploit at Michilimackinac he reproduced verbatim from the somewhat gaudy original narrative of its hero, a practice he later became skillful enough to avoid. In selecting his material he tended to minimize factors which did not suit his interest in the heroic. And his style, while a good deal more skillful than anything he had previously done, binds the work more closely to *The Oregon Trail* than to his final works. Rhetorical flourishes and a feverish profusion of adjectives obscure a narrative which he would later learn to present without ambiguity or mannerism. Likewise Parkman had yet to solve problems of character. Pontiac emerges both as every inch an Indian and as a close approximation to a Greek hero, at once in and out of his own culture. His stature in relation to the theme of the book is exaggerated even with respect to what Parkman's own sources revealed as well as to what modern scholarship has established.[14] The character of Maj. Robert Rogers here reflects Parkman's idealization of the forest fighter; later, in *Montcalm and Wolfe,* he was reduced to a more proportionate size in the order of things.

For all of this *Pontiac* marked in the United States a distinct advance in research and writing. As literary art it could scarcely

14. See particularly Howard Peckham, *Pontiac and the Indian Uprising* (Princeton, 1947), pp. 108–110.

challenge such contemporary classics as *The Scarlet Letter*, *Moby Dick*, *Representative Men*, or *Walden*. But as history, with the possible exception of Prescott's works, it had no American rival. The research alone had been staggering. Parkman had digested more than three thousand pages of original documents, collected or copied, including numerous journals and contemporary accounts. Even more significant was his use of the archives in London and Paris and, a special source, the Cass Papers in Michigan.[15] The finished study promised much for his work to come. Not only did Parkman demonstrate an awareness of the interaction of one society and culture on another. He made of the conflict of two colonies under the determining influences of the wilderness a modified frontier thesis for colonial history. And not least of all he presented Indian warriors, for perhaps the first time, not as contemporary literature showed them but as the cruel, violent, vacillating, childish savages which the English settlers had experienced and described.

Parkman also showed that he was narrowing the gap between the reality of what he had experienced and the framework of historical actuality. Perhaps the most impressive literary passage in the work occurs in a chapter describing the horrors and desolation of Indian warfare on the Pennsylvania frontier. Picturing the plight of white captives following a raid, he imagines one as having escaped in the night from the Indian's camp on the trail, losing his way in the tangled wilderness, circling back on his tracks, and in desperation climbing a tree to locate his position. "Dark, wild, and lonely, the wilderness stretches around him, half hidden in clouds, half open to the sight, mountain and valley, crag and glistening stream; but nowhere can he discern the trace of human hand. . . ." Descending, he wanders blindly. "Nothing can be seen but the same endless monotony of brown trunks and green leaves, closing him in with an impervious screen." Finally, Parkman writes, he may stumble onto

15. See *Pontiac, 1,* xi–xii.

a settlement, or he may perish, "a meager banquet for the wolves." [16]

Here is an incident "made to order" by Parkman himself. In presenting a hypothetical case of a common but unspecified historical situation, he avoided the necessity of having to re-create the event as history. This device he seldom used else-where, preferring usually to integrate any generalized experi-ence with a specific example from the records. Yet artistically the incident is valid, and it fulfills a vital requirement for the embellishment of historical material: it conforms to all of the known facts. In this early period of his writing Parkman thus foreshadowed his final achievement, the fusion of historical fact with artistic perception, giving in combination meaning to the one and augmented validity to the other.

16. *Pontiac*, 2, 101. It should be noted that the manuscript of *Pontiac* (which Parkman dictated to assistants) contains a passage of nearly eleven pages in which practically no verbal or structural changes or emendations appear. Included in this section is the pas-sage under discussion. The evidence suggests, but not conclusively, that Parkman dictated this particular passage directly from the memory of an experience, and that its excitement and tension are his own. See "The Conspiracy of Pontiac, letter-press copy, from chap-ter 21 to end, corrections by F. P.," Francis Parkman Papers, Vol. *86*, Massachusetts Historical Society.

CHAPTER TWO

Version of Truth

What men call history is the idea they have of the
past, not the actual events they never witnessed.
—PERRY MILLER, *Jonathan Edwards*

Pontiac was not long completed when Parkman turned to
his major project, but critical illness interrupted work, and
it was not until 1862 that the histories began to develop rapidly.[1]
In 1864 he could say that "most of the material [for the series]
is collected or within reach."[2] *The Pioneers of France in the*
New World appeared in 1865, *The Jesuits in North America in*
the Seventeenth Century in 1867, and *The Discovery of the*
Great West in 1869. He had half finished a fourth work on Count
Frontenac, but delayed it in order to publish as the "middle"
volume of the series his researches on New France as a colony,
a subject less easily rendered than the material on Frontenac
and no doubt less palatable to him. *The Old Régime in Canada*
appeared in 1874, and *Count Frontenac and New France under*
Louis XIV followed in 1877; in 1878 Parkman revised his third
book upon gaining access to some long-awaited source material
secreted by Father Margry at the Archives of the Marine and
Colonies in Paris. Re-entitled *La Salle and the Discovery of the*

1. Parkman wrote his only novel in this period. *Vassall Morton*
(Boston, 1856) was based, significantly enough, on autobiography
and personal experience.
2. Letter to Dr. Ellis, 1864, Parkman Papers, Massachusetts Historical Society.

Great West it was to run through eleven editions. Following *Frontenac* Parkman, then fifty-five, determined to write what he had originally planned in 1841 to be the central episode in the series. It appeared in 1884 as *Montcalm and Wolfe,* twice the length of the others. Revision of *Pioneers* in 1885 came as a result of new material and a personal trip to Florida. *A Half-Century of Conflict* completed the series in 1892, save for fifty pages of addenda to *The Old Régime* in 1893, the year of his death.

The exhaustiveness of his research and the extent of his collected sources were in all likelihood unmatched by an American writer of his century. He had compiled and sifted the bulk of his sources before he had begun any of the series, and with material flowing in to the end of his life, he was always ready to revise his work when new sources became available. For the 16th and 17th centuries, in addition to the Jesuit *Rélations* and the contemporary accounts in Hakluyt and others, he had access to quantities of material from the Spanish, French, and Canadian archives, private journals and accounts, the writings of Champlain, the Sparks Papers (on La Salle), and the correspondence between the colony and France on military, ecclesiastical, mercantile, and governmental matters, as well as state and private collections in America. For his last volumes he drew on British archives and colonial records from Nova Scotia to the West Indies. Some six thousand pages of documents from France and ten volumes from England, added to a great number of private papers, such as Montcalm's letters, underlay the writing of *Montcalm and Wolfe.* By 19th-century standards Parkman's books are adequately annotated, the earlier volumes with greater detail than those which followed. A critical bibliography appears in *Pioneers,* and a bibliographical essay on 17th-century maps of the Mississippi Valley concludes *La Salle.* He wrote lengthy appendices for five of the seven books; though the materials in them are not integral to the main texts of the histories, they serve the reader as samples of Parkman's sources and occasionally include data on subjects controversial in his day, such as the British role in the Acadian exodus, or Washington's meeting with Villiers over the death of Jumonville.

Parkman's prefaces and introductions offer valuable clues to changes in the theme of his books; in some instances the books themselves reveal less of the theme than do the prefaces. I have discussed the theme of *Pontiac*. In 1865 Parkman outlined a new theme, or rather formalized one implicit in what had gone before. New France and New England stand opposed as examples of differing national character, each of which "followed its natural laws of growth, and each came to its natural result." [3] France grew no roots in the new world. Her colony was imposing, but rotten at the core. She tried to "grasp a continent" and failed. England sent forth material roots. Her colonies, if feeble in appearance, grew strong with prosperity, liberty, and self-reliance. England won a continent. The outcome of the struggle had thus the certainty of a biological process. Twelve years later, in 1877, Parkman elaborated his hypothesis as follows:

> In *The Old Régime in Canada* I tried to show from what inherent causes this wilderness empire of the Great Monarch fell at last before a foe, superior indeed in numbers, but lacking all the forces that belong to a system of civil and military centralization. The present volume [*Frontenac*] will show how valiantly, and for a time how successfully, New France battled against a fate which her own organic fault made inevitable. [4]

By 1884, however, Parkman had come to regard the struggle between the two colonies as one for maritime, and hence commercial, supremacy of the entire world; in the introduction to

3. *Pioneers of France in the New World* (Boston, Little, Brown and Co., 1903), *1*, xcvi. First ed. 1865. Hereafter cited as *Pioneers*.
4. *Count Frontenac and New France under Louis XIV* (Boston, Little, Brown and Co., 1903), p. xiii. First ed. 1877. Hereafter cited as *Frontenac*.

14911

Montcalm and Wolfe he indicated that the outcome of the conflict stemmed as much from the policies of war conducted by the
two nations in Europe as from the internal "character" of the
colonies.[5] That he regarded the emphasis on international dis-
putes as consistent with his theory of "character" is evident from
his comment in 1892 concerning *A Half-Century of Conflict*.
His final work was meant, he said, to illustrate "the singularly
contrasted characters and methods of the rival claimants to
North America," the claimants being not only the colonies but
the two European powers as well.[6]

Parkman's seven books clearly form a single history and may
be so analyzed and judged. It is to be regretted that he did not
"file and burnish and cut out whatever is superfluous," as Henry
Adams advised him to do.[7] The history would have profited from
such a process, though the books individually might have lost
some of their inner unity. I find little evidence that Parkman
was significantly influenced by the ferment in American historical scholarship seething around him. His last book differs from
his first in ways explicable by reference to Parkman's maturing
literary facility and by little else. *Montcalm and Wolfe* owed
nothing to the new "scientific history"; Parkman's tradition and
his achievement were distinctly his own. Though he transcended
the "middle school" of historians, he scarcely belonged to the
new school. Where he actually stood can be determined only
by an analysis of the histories themselves.

The subject which unifies all seven books is "the story of
New France." Either chronological or topical continuity with
regard to New France would suggest an arrangement of material
rather different from Parkman's, which emphasized special

5. *Montcalm and Wolfe* (Boston, Little, Brown and Co., 1903), *1*,
6. First ed. 1884. Hereafter cited as *M. and W.*

6. *A Half-Century of Conflict* (Boston, Little, Brown and Co.,
1903), *1*, preface. First ed. 1892. Hereafter cited as *Half-Century*.

7. Adams to Parkman, December 21, 1884. Francis Parkman
Papers, Massachusetts Historical Society.

literary and dramatic interests. For one thing he delayed treatment of the background of French colonization. The Huguenot
colony in Florida and its brutal denouement greet the reader
with an initial impact and shock that plunges him into the
middle of action. As in a carefully conceived drama this opening
incident foreshadows the entire series, narrating the exploits of
heroes and wretches in unfamiliar forests and the ambiguous
relations between colonials and savages. The story of Florida is
also an aberration from the principal stream of events; placing
it first clears the stage for the main plot.

To present the origins of New France Parkman utilized the
device of biography. In his account of Champlain he focused the
initial colonization and discovery, the frightful winters in
Canada, and a preliminary glimpse of the Iroquois and Hurons.
The second book brings together the Indian and the Jesuit; the
drama of rival cultures underlies the account of the first missionaries and their heroic achievements. Interrupting this action
appear sixty pages describing the commercial and secular beginnings of Quebec, but before the digression can engage our
interest we are plunged into the climax of the book—the martyrdom of the Jesuit priests and the destruction of the Huron nation.

Parkman's next subject was practically made to order for
him. The story of La Salle embodied a rise, climax, denouement,
and tragic decline, offering a dramatic structure ideal for fusing
literary with historical interest. Beneath the drama runs a unify-
ing theme—the lure of the West and the importance of this lure
to French colonization. But in his haste to cover this intrinsically
dramatic material Parkman left several vital gaps both in place
and time which he had now to fill in. La Salle's story occurred
in the 1680's and belonged to the later period of Frontenac's
regime. Between 1640 and 1680 the colony of the St. Lawrence
Valley grew, first as a Jesuit mission, then under royal secular
administration. In Acadia strange events occurred having little
relation to anything else in New France. For purposes of organ-

izing integrated books, each with its dramatic issue, Parkman
concentrated the economic and institutional material, a barrier
to narrative interest, into *The Old Régime*, a midpoint and a
watershed for the series. By 1670 the distinctive permanent
character of New France had taken shape—its internal struggles
between priest, soldier, and merchant, its geographical dichot-
omy between fur trade and agriculture, and the growing in-
compatibility between French colonial policy and the needs
and interests of the permanent colonists. In a single volume,
then, are to be found all of the material which Parkman feared
might otherwise mar the dramatic flow and unity of the patterns
which he was most interested in re-creating. If the reader feels
uncomfortable at the hodgepodge of history in *The Old Régime*,
he must admit that much of it could scarcely have gone anywhere else.

At this point the chronology sails clear. The life of Frontenac
provides a unity for describing the next critical period of the
colony. But though biography forms the structure of *Frontenac*,
the necessities of history constantly break through with interests and events critical to the understanding of the more flam-
boyant drama on the surface. French power had built up to a
point of stalemate vis-à-vis the Iroquois and the English, while
on the Upper Lakes French commerce consolidated its position.
Other themes important in the later books emerged in this
period: the clash of rival empires in border war; the rivalry for
western lands and the control of trade; the relative eclipse of
the Indian as a major power in the conflict; and the growing
strength of the English colonies, tested by warfare which raged
intermittently until 1760.

It seems clear that Parkman arranged the presentation of his
facts to bring out certain basic themes possessing a deep attrac-
tion for him. First of all he chronicled the violent exploits of the
16th- and early 17th-century explorers, whose semimedieval
world had long captured his imagination. Second, he traced the
slow destruction of the Indian culture and its wilderness en-

vironment; these, as we have seen, had been Parkman's most thoroughly romanticized early interests. Third, Parkman analyzed the Catholic universe with a mixture of approbation and denunciation that he seldom took pains to disguise; the 18th-century priest is the most villainous character type in the entire series, while his early 17th-century predecessors rank high in a long list of heroes. Fourth, the secular individuals whose characters and exploits Parkman had most wanted to narrate throng every chapter and carry the thread of every action. And last, under the drama and action, providing a structure of the logic, as opposed to the life, of history, lies the web of institutional and economic fact. Parkman might have chosen to delineate and emphasize the web as one studying anatomy might cut away the flesh to reveal the skeleton. Yet for the mid-19th-century historians history was more than the skeleton; it was the living body, and Parkman does not seem to have been thoroughly happy until, having disposed of the economic structure, he could turn to his real interests. I wish to examine in turn each of the major historical themes in Parkman's history and his arrangement of them.

THE FIRST EXPLORERS

By 1600 a few Frenchmen may have been touched by the commercial and intellectual currents of the modern era, but on the sailor and fisherman, the common soldier and the explorer the medieval world and its unseen demonism still held a firm grip. Bretons and Normans had knocked about the New World shores for several generations, setting up their huts on the rock strands of Newfoundland. While they brought back fish for Catholic Europe at a material profit, they also told of griffins and monsters and other spirits of the sea. Life was cheap, cruel, and frightful in its misery for those who tried to spend the winters in that country. Yet within a few years the feudal chiefs in search

of wilderness kingdoms to be based on furs and metals induced
bands of adventurers to follow them and settle. The soldiers
and explorers ruled their settlements with the power of life and
death. Champlain was once warned of insubordination in his
command. He captured the ringleader, whose body, says Parkman, soon after "swinging from a gibbet, gave wholesome warn-
ing to those he had seduced; and his head was displayed on a
pike, from the highest roof of the buildings, food for birds and
a lesson to sedition." [8] Perhaps the plotter was lucky. In the
misery of winter months, with sub-zero temperatures and with
winds cutting down from Arctic wastes, food supplies gave out
and disease carried off all but a handful of the colonists. Nevertheless they clung, seeking a way to India, seeking wealth or a
kingdom for the church, or possessed perhaps by qualities of
medieval crusaders.

Champlain seems to have embodied all of these motives. A
devout believer and a reckless explorer, he combined scientific
curiosity with a credulity that induced him to record the exist-
ence both of coast lines and sea griffins.[9] Commercial support
for his ventures periodically failed him, or, more properly, he
and his fellow colonizers failed to produce the profits expected
of them. Anarchy in the fur trade lent its typical color to the
St. Lawrence area; by 1611 competition had become literally
cutthroat, and Champlain soon lost control of his infant settlement at Quebec. Moving west he anticipated a century of vision-
aries with his dreams of a vast political kingdom on the upper
river, significantly in alliance with, not control over, the Indian
tribes. The courage he displayed in journeying with a tiny band
to the country of the Hurons, the first white man ever to go so
far, scarcely exceeded his rashness in joining an Algonquin war
party against some Iroquois on the lake later named after him.
He was to persist in an arduous struggle against the wilderness
environment until, before dying in 1635, he saw established at

8. *Pioneers*, 2, 158.
9. *Ibid.*, p. 61.

Quebec a tiny but firm colony, drawing its strength from the Récollet and Jesuit orders and, more important, from the French mercantile interests of Richelieu.

The coercive force of the wilderness itself imparts vividness to the account of unfamiliar men remote in time. Because of Parkman's skilled objectivity in reporting, the surface impressions of forest and Indian on the medieval mind become the reader's impressions. Champlain's first encounter with Indians owes something to Parkman's own first encounter with them in the Laramie Mountains. Champlain learned of their treachery, their fickleness, their material interest in economic goods, their demonic interest in all else. He also learned from them how to fight and to live on the edge of the forest, where cultural patterns were often reduced to primitivism. A magnificent scene of Champlain lost in the forest is based on the bald facts from his journal.[10] It is reinforced by Parkman's own experience; both the situation and the details of the forest scene could have been re-enacted at almost any time from 1600 to the present. If Champlain becomes real to us through Parkman's identification with him, then so does the history of his time. For Champlain symbolizes the adventurers of his age and their endeavors to found a New France. That its descendant culture seemed older in 1760 than that of Old France bears out Parkman's perception of the medieval nature of its beginnings.

THE INDIANS

At one episode of Indian cruelty Champlain was so revolted that he could not bear to witness it. His Indian allies, for whom he had just killed two Iroquois enemies, began to scalp alive one of their prisoners taken in the fight. Parkman added, "The scene filled [Champlain] with horror; but a few months later, on the Place de la Grève at Paris, he might have witnessed tor-

10. *Ibid.*, pp. 239–40.

tures equally vindictive, inflicted on the regicide Ravaillac by
the sentence of grave and learned judges." [11] Parkman often
tempered his portraits of the Indian with penetrating comments
on medieval and Stone Age cultures. Never did he condone
Indian mores, but in suggesting that savagery is present in any
culture and often thinly hidden he made it clear that the Indians
were not so blameworthy or depraved as their observers sup-
posed. Parkman's critics have declared that he viewed Indians
too much as the pioneer and the settler did, that he was too
harsh on them. Whatever the merits of this criticism one conclusion is evident. Parkman's harsh judgment fell not upon the
Indian, who knew no better, but upon the medieval savagery
of the Jesuit priests and their military partisans who abetted
and encouraged border slaughter. These men plainly did know
better and, what is more, professed to be better. The Indian
saw no moral wrong in his methods of warfare. Parkman judged
Indian brutality not as reprehensible but as a tragedy of circumstance and a cold lesson in power for the weakly defended
colonists. If his Indians appear to skulk like inhuman beasts near
the window of a frontier cabin, it is because they appeared so
to the settlers. History may well be written more effectively
from inside the window, as it were, than from on high. Likewise
if his Indians are squalid and dirty and behave in their bark huts
like animals, if their loyalties seem to depend on the authority
of an owl's tooth or the lure of firearms and cheap rum, who is
to gainsay what Parkman had seen for himself and what any
French trapper or English trader could verify? When the historian adds gratuitously that the Indian race was "lower" than
the white race, that it was "higher" than the "servile" races, or
that their sexual customs were "shameless," [12] one may deplore
his assertions and discount them; but his picture of the Indian is

11. *Ibid.*, p. 177.
12. *The Jesuits in North America in the Seventeenth Century*
(Boston, Little, Brown and Co., 1903), *1*, 21. First ed., 1867. Hereafter cited as *Jesuits*.

not thereby damaged. One's conclusions from the picture merely differ from Parkman's.

The Indians played a complex role in the story of New France. The early Jesuits were the first to analyze and to understand their patterns of behavior. Parkman's analysis of them relied not only on his own research but on the incredibly objective accounts left by the Jesuits themselves. With no incentive to deceive their ecclesiastical superiors, with no chance for personal gain, and with the strongest interest in probing the Indian mind that they might win the soul, the Jesuits established a body of knowledge of Indian culture that is still widely respected in our own day. The account, however, is fairly closely confined to the Iroquois and Huron nations and is less relevant to the period after 1700. By 1640 the French had gambled on winning the friendship of the Hurons and western tribes, a gamble which cost them the inevitable wrath of the Iroquois. Like a storm the Iroquois laid waste French settlements and nearly destroyed the commercial basis of the colony. All efforts of the French to appease them proved unsuccessful. They traded instead with the English and Dutch, and they resented French alliances with their western rivals, for they were thereby deprived of the position of middlemen. Their own exhaustion and decimation and the increased power of French regular troops under Tracy and Frontenac finally eliminated them as a potent factor in colonial rivalry, but not before they in turn had virtually wiped out the Hurons and Eries to the west.

In the 18th century as colonial rivalry grew the Indian declined in political importance. The center of tribal power shifted to the Ohio Valley and the Upper Lakes. Because Parkman's treatment of the West after 1700 was scanty, the Indian's role in the later books became merely that of a "Christianized" partisan satellite in French border warfare. The use which the French made of the Abenakis affords hideous reading, softened only partially by Parkman's explanation that to have failed to keep them stirred up to bloodshed against the English would

have meant their mass defection and the resultant loss of French
influence over the western tribes, a rationalization for which
Parkman had little sympathy. Parkman was scornful of the
failure of the English to evolve a constructive Indian policy, but
the evidence of Pontiac's disillusionment with his English
"brothers" makes one wonder whether it was ever in the nature
of English colonization to have a constructive policy. To the
end of the period the French remained the Indians' most consistent friends.

The Indian dwelt in an animistic world. Irrational by white
standards, his conduct conformed to the logic of his own beliefs.
To live was of less importance than to die with tested endurance
and in contempt of pain. The infliction of pain, cruelty, or death
was no more reprehensible than hunting or playing, and infi-
nitely less so than betraying weakness by reluctance to do these
things. The Indian respected only power and dignity. (Parkman
could write this with relish!) He feared only the demonic world.
Memory was embodied in legends, fantasy, and tribal myth
rather than in rationalized experience. In avenging a wrong or
an injury the Indian was ruthless and persevering. His relations to his tribe and his kin were highly patterned. He recognized hierarchy, but only as a structure; the individuals compos-
ing it might be changed at any time for almost any reason. No
concerted, sustained group effort was ever certain. Though the
Iroquois developed a somewhat more sophisticated political
framework than their neighbors, their behavior was generally
no less atomistic, and even they, Parkman suggested, were
probably incapable of existing as an independent nation in an
agricultural complex: of all of the Indian tribal patterns of behavior theirs were the most highly specialized and inflexible.
Jesuit missions among them met with even slighter success than
elsewhere.

Parkman re-created scenes of Indian life, their pageantry
and councils and speeches, with the realism of direct observation. In reproducing Indian oratory the literary historian can

indulge his taste for rhetoric and yet remain substantially true to fact. The high colors of the imagery are echoed in the overt ceremonies that accompany them. The Indians did not easily formulate abstractions or concepts. Such qualities they commonly expressed by metaphors direct from nature, and Parkman made the most of documented Indian speeches. Equally skillful was his rendering of a scene in an Indian village introduced into the story of La Salle from a specific experience of Parkman's own. The prose, setting forth only observable fact, possesses the almost photographic clarity of a painting by Bodmer or Catlin.

> Enter one of their dwellings . . . and study the lodge and its inmates by the light that streams through the holes at the top. Three or four fires smoke and smoulder on the ground down the middle of the long arched structure. . . . A squaw sits weaving a mat of rushes; a warrior, naked except his moccasins, and tattooed with fantastic devices, binds a stone arrow-head to its shaft, with the fresh sinews of a buffalo. Some lie asleep, some sit staring in vacancy, some are eating, some are squatted in lazy chat around a fire. The smoke brings water to your eyes; the fleas annoy you; small unkempt children, naked as young puppies, crawl about your knees and will not be repelled.[13]

In such a manner as this Parkman's eye offered his readers what all of his analysis of the Indian's mind failed to do—an experience of his presence.

THE CHURCH

Throughout the 17th century the Catholic Church was the most powerful institution in New France. Under Frontenac a growing

13. *La Salle and the Discovery of the Great West* (Boston, Little Brown and Co., 1903), pp. 221-2. First published in 1869 as *The Discovery of the Great West*. Hereafter cited as *La Salle*.

military force fed by French secular authority tended to reduce
its role. But at the peak of Catholic domination under Bishop
Laval, the priest class ran the colony as it pleased. Priests had
first arrived with Champlain. By 1623 these early Récollet friars
were superseded by a more powerful order, the Jesuits. It is their
mind and their spirit which Parkman tried most fully to understand, for their order became the controlling ecclesiastical force
in the colony.

Parkman never disguised his enthusiasm for military virtues,
whether in a person or in a social structure, and though he de-
plored the Jesuits' doctrine, he seems to have found to his liking
their soldierly dedication and discipline and their seeming in-
difference to material calamity or to personal affliction. Their
founder, a medieval soldier, had become a militant, active
crusader. The first Jesuits in Canada were agents only of God
and the Church, and one cannot fully understand their heroic
missions among the Hurons except in terms of the total reality
of the Catholic universe. Parkman sensed the power of this
universe in remarkable passages doubtless inspired by the *Rélations*. Despite his contempt for Jesuit beliefs, he also conveyed
something of the coercive force which these beliefs had exercised upon them, and he concluded how easy it must have been
for illusion to become reality under the compulsive stresses of
Jesuit devotion. The Jesuits lived for one object, the conversion
of souls; nothing else mattered. Success or failure alike had one
result: return to the work at hand; martyrdom was rather to
be welcomed than feared. As missionaries they surpassed all
others in adapting themselves to wilderness and Indian life.
They pushed, paddled, or stumbled through winter and summer, hundreds of miles, to the Michigan and Wisconsin shores,
to the Hurons, and even to the Iroquois. They lived where they
could and as they could. They became as knowledgeable in the
ways of the wilderness as the trappers and traders. Yet their
minds seemed unaffected. They carried with them the Catholic
world of their boyhood and monastery training. Alone of all

the white men they sought to add to the Indian culture without disrupting it. Easy though it was for the Jesuits to convert Indians, permanent conversions were not numerous. The Indians proved equally adept at forgetting their faith in a day or week; they often merely added the Catholic demonology to their own and used it as they would a new gadget. This curious contact between the Indian and Jesuit mind Parkman explored to the fullest, both because of its intrinsic interest and because it had been important in furthering French colonial policy. The priests gained the trust and confidence of many tribes and were often the only reliable contact between Indian and colonial authority. One permanent change in Indian life they did achieve: Indian barbarities in warfare, notably the practice of cannibalism, were greatly modified in the areas where the Jesuit missions had flourished.

Parkman found in the Jesuit story the kind of material which he most liked to narrate. He has pictured the black-gowned fathers ploughing through the slush of spring snow to reach a wretched native village. There they sat coughing in smoky tents, eyes red and swollen, baptizing infants on the sly or outtalking Indians whose imagery and rhetoric could scarcely match the scholastic vividness of dedicated priests. They lived in hourly peril of death. Indian caprice and whim might wreak on a Jesuit torture and humiliation where yesterday he had been administering sacraments to anxious converts. Parkman was also apt to describe with humor the foibles of priests and believers. When a priest wrote of his satisfaction at the Christian virtues of Membertou, an Acadian chief who had been converted at the age of one hundred and contented himself thenceforth with but one wife, Parkman pointed out that for a centenarian it was "hardly a superlative merit." [14] The Sulpicians of Montreal were perpetually circulating tales of miracles, mostly to the glory of martyred members of their own order. For example, a Sulpician missionary was beheaded by savages, and both head

14. *Pioneers*, 2, 117.

and stump refused to bleed. The Jesuits of Quebec, however, refused to credit Sulpician miracles and neglected to report this one to the pope, a carelessness which for a while caused bitter feeling.[15] One incident revealing an attitude among the working classes toward priests concerned a ship's crew which (a priest related with horror), upon reaching shore in 1604, buried the bodies of a Catholic priest and a Huguenot minister "both in one grave to see if they would lie peaceably together." [16]

Parkman found less to his humor in later phases of the Jesuit story. By 1660 the Church militant had become a tool for political sovereignty over New France, a development symbolized most clearly in the career of Laval, an ultramontane priest who, though not a Jesuit himself, served the purposes of the Jesuits all his life. The history of Quebec in these years Parkman interpreted as the result of a seesaw conflict for power in France between the Roman and the Gallican parties in the Church. Laval as Bishop of Quebec, a member of the ruling triumvirate in Canada, consolidated his power by "breaking" every royal governor who came over to administer colonial affairs. The governors subsequently either cooperated and were cut in on the economic profits which the merchants, priests, and petty officials combined to squeeze out of the colony, or they were generally recalled for failure to get anything done. Gross peculation and fraud marked the Canadian government from beginning to end. When Frontenac more or less dethroned Laval and his priests, no change in the system resulted, merely a change in the profiteers. Laval's greatest achievement was to establish a seminary for priests in Quebec and to vest himself with absolute powers of recall over local curés—two moves which practically assured the supremacy of the Canadian bishop in local ecclesiastical matters and allowed the Jesuit Order to win

15. *The Old Régime in Canada* (Boston, Little, Brown and Co., 1903), *1*, iii. First ed. 1874. Hereafter cited as *Old Régime*.
16. *Pioneers, 2,* 69.

fairly complete control over the personal lives of the settled population.[17]

By the 18th century the Jesuits had become a tool of the political authority in France and Canada. They stirred up and organized their Indians in a long succession of raids on New England settlements; they worked side by side with military officers in furthering French commercial and military interests. Parkman's treatment of these agents is savage but accurate and hardly unjust. A foremost representative of this breed was Sebastien Rale, a missionary who exercised his talents mostly in organizing Abenakis into butchering parties along the Maine border, condoning and encouraging them by means of his functions as a priest.[18] In the thread of Parkman's story the temporal influence of the church virtually disappeared by 1750, its power an adjunct of the state. Its importance in determining the absolutist character of the colony and in excluding all non-Catholic settlers, however, Parkman considered critical in shaping the character of modern French Canada.

THE LEADERS AND THEIR HEROISM

If one were asked to point to a single theme sustaining the thread of action through Parkman's writings one's simplest reply would be the actions of heroic men. Action allowed Parkman to write at his best pitch of style. The reasons by now should be obvious. His earliest writings had glorified individuals. His biographers attest his lifelong devotion to Scott, Byron, and Cooper. These romantic writers were gifted in character portrayal, and, more specifically, in creating the solitary hero who fought his own way through obstacles and misfortune on the strength of what Parkman would call nobility, integrity, and manliness of spirit. Such a hero was apt to hover on the

17. *Old Régime*, *1*, 165 ff. and *2*, 153.
18. *Half-Century*, *1*, 214–40, *passim*.

fringe of civilized order: a warrior in the Scottish highlands, an outlaw wanderer in remote lands, or a heroic frontier-and-forest hunter, combining the virtues of two cultures and the vices of neither. It is clear how close Parkman felt himself to such men. Their exploits had occurred under conditions which he had taken great pains to rediscover and experience. The history of New France provided as fact not only the men but the exploits, which romantic novelists and poets often had to create. Parkman's re-creation of historically valid individuals was enhanced by his power to identify himself with them.

The most striking element which the historic heroes possessed in common was the courage and sagacity with which they faced the unknown. The wilderness forced them to live in elemental directness; the values which meant survival were the very ones which Parkman believed basic for mankind. In reviewing the works of Cooper in 1852 he had declared his admiration for Leatherstocking in these terms: "There is something admirably felicitous in the conception of this hybrid offspring of civilization and barbarism, in whom uprightness, kindliness, innate philosophy, and the truest moral perceptions are joined with the wandering instincts and hatred of restraint which stamp the Indian or the Bedouin. . . . Where the moral instincts are originally strong, they may find nutriment and growth among the rude scenes and grand associations of the wilderness." [19] With savage virtues had to go brilliant discipline of mind, trained in civilized virtues. "A gentleman of the right sort will stand hardship better than anybody else," a Rocky Mountain trapper once said to Parkman.[20] All of the men whom Parkman celebrated possess the martial spirit, and most were actually soldiers. They were capable, even brilliant improvisers; history revealed them as fit to cope with the chaos and uncertainty of life in the wilderness.

The most outstanding figures in Parkman's history, other

19. *The North American Review, 74* (January, 1852), 151.
20. *La Salle,* p. 198, n.

than Champlain, are La Salle and Frontenac. No other figure can match either of them. Of the two La Salle's impact on the reader is significantly much the greater. Frontenac's career was more alien to Parkman's experiences and was inextricably woven into the politics of French colonial administration. La Salle was a creature of more epic proportions, and the account of his life is almost Homeric. Intense ambition and a restless energy possessed him; he was captured by the visions of his age—a passage to India, an inland empire, conquest of the Mexican mines—each superseding the other as, one by one, they proved illusory. Though he had every material incentive to remain at Fort Frontenac in a feudal tenure as one of Frontenac's lieutenants, he was impelled to organize and lead one expedition after another into the Illinois and Mississippi valleys enduring incredible reverses of fortune. Deceit, treachery, weather, rivals, and Indians set him back year after year. He would have failed entirely were it not for Tonty, his assistant, a scarcely less heroic figure in his own right, and more agreeable.

La Salle's relations with the men who served under him (and here Parkman is cryptically brief) form one continuous tale of resentment, mutiny, and abuse. He led by force of will and courageous example, but he plainly had no sympathy for subordinates and entertained a well-founded suspicion of all others. Frontenac alone tried to save his schemes from dissolution. It is notorious that Parkman himself took little interest in the lower-class strata which supported his heroes and their exploits; and he offered his readers no clue to the attitudes of the men under La Salle. Consider, for example, the nonchalance with which, at one place, Parkman hinted at the tension and strain between La Salle and his band. For fully ten pages preceding the following passage one finds not a hint of disagreement or trouble: "In the morning, the party shouldered their canoes and baggage and began their march for the sources of the river Illinois, some five miles distant. . . . As they filed on

their way, a man named Duplessis, bearing a grudge against
La Salle, who walked just before him, raised his gun to shoot
him through the back, but was prevented by one of his comrades. They soon reached . . . the sources of the Illinois." [21]
There is no further reference to the incident. The promise of a
gripping episode in human relations tantalizes the reader with
what the record omits. Surely Parkman need not have been so
unperturbed and urbane in telling of Duplessis! What sort of
man was La Salle, who could stir up such a "grudge" as this
against himself? What happened to Duplessis? Was he perhaps
summarily "prevented" ever from raising his gun again? Parkman's tone of voice plays down but can scarcely hide the am-
biguities in La Salle's leadership.

La Salle's last expedition to the Gulf coast underlay one of
the most gripping dramas in the entire history. The details of his
search for the river and his eventual assassination are of interest
in themselves; but, though the expedition failed, the account
of its preparations and intrigues offer added value, for it reveals
much about French colonial enterprises—particularly their dependence on favoritism and influence at court, as well as occasional royal whim. And beyond the historical narrative rises the
supreme tragedy of La Salle himself—a man whose obsession
with an idea and whose reversal of fortunes combined to deprive
him of his judgment and in the end perhaps his very reason. He
drove his colonists to a wretched fate and himself into a realm
of dreams and unreal projects. His was almost the monomania
of Melville's Ahab, and it was Parkman's genius to have been
able to combine the epic qualities in La Salle's heroic career
with the objective simplicity of historical prose.

La Salle, however, seems almost democratic compared to
Frontenac. Imperious, autocratic to a ludicrous degree, Frontenac nevertheless possessed two virtues which his colony badly
needed: the sheer force with which he ruled New France, and
his extraordinary ability to command the respect and even the

21. *La Salle*, p. 166.

obedience of the Indians. More than a soldier and courtier, he was also a shrewd politician with an instinct for commercial opportunities in colonial government. He could probably have outtalked any Indian orator east of the Lakes, and his withering reply to Phips' agent, sent while the New England fleet lay ominously off the rock of Quebec, was a splendid exercise in diplomatic swordplay.[22] As rendered by Parkman the questions of prerogative in pew sitting, council room, and outdoor greetings—all of them clashes between church and state—take on the significance of important institutional history and yet remain satisfyingly anecdotal. But despite an abundance of colorful material Parkman's presentation of Frontenac betrays weaknesses. One cannot resist the suspicion, for example, that the melodramatic cast of certain pages oversimplifies the political complexities in the career of one who, after all, dominated a turbulent frontier colony for the better part of twenty years. Is it not also likely that Frontenac's haughty arrogance sprang more from a pose, self-consciously cultivated, than from inner character? The French background to Frontenac's life, sketched in the opening chapters, is at best a superficial mélange of unconvincing personalities and intrigues more worthy of a Scott novel than a Parkman history. Nevertheless Parkman seldom wrote such incisive and powerful prose as may be found in the later pages of *Frontenac,* and his final judgment of the man is restrained and candid.

Parkman's interest in character bestowed an equally heroic flavor on a host of lesser men. Although Montcalm and Wolfe attained the dignity of a title page, neither was treated with the fullness accorded the three already discussed. Part of the reason may be attributed to the fact that interest in the events of the Seven Years' War overshadows the individuals who fought in it; nevertheless the galaxy of leaders is striking—Pepperell, Shirley, Johnson, Washington, Vaudreuil, Pitt, Amherst, Bouquet. Some are less ably drawn than others, for in presenting

22. *Frontenac,* pp. 265 ff.

men whose lives were absorbed by military and political operations and by problems of colonial economics, Parkman could
not rely on his own experience. When chronicling the wilderness exploit or the heroic partisan enterprise he conveyed to
his pages more of the immediacy of the event. Rogers' Rangers,
it is recalled, had been the first subject Parkman ever attempted
in print, and in his earlier books these lesser incidents provided
excitement and entertainment worthy of the most improbable
fiction, told with the relish of one who craved similar adventures
for himself. One recalls his tale of Dominique de Gourgues, who
hazarded a fabulous expedition for revenge on the Spaniards
purely for love of adventure, or at least the record, obscured
by three centuries, revealed to Parkman no other earthly motive.
Isaac Jogues, the greatest Jesuit figure in the history, returned
a second time from his escape to face certain death at Iroquois
hands. Piskaret, the Algonquin warrior, performed legendary
exploits unexcelled by any of Cooper's Indians but fortunately
verified by the *Rélations*. The battle in which twenty French
youths fought to the last man against six hundred attacking
Indians at the "Long Saut" occurred in the precarious days when
scarcely 2,500 people inhabited the entire colony; it was the
heroic age in which Dollier de Casson, the "fighting priest" of
St. Anne, carried his own portable chapel on his back from settlement to settlement lest God's work suffer neglect. A historian
such as Parkman who relived his dreams so powerfully and on
such terms of actuality had only to find the corresponding image
and the drive of words to carry his readers headlong with him.

One ought not to conclude that Parkman was so wrapped up
in his enthusiasms as to lose perspective on his subject. To
the re-creation of the heroic he brought a trenchant sense of
humor. He readily spotted the ludicrous, the ironic, and the
pompous. Furthermore he possessed, it seems, a half-savage en-
joyment of situations themselves comic although scarcely considered comic at the time. The small vessel which carried Champlain from France on his second momentous voyage in 1610

made a "prosperous" crossing, "no other mishap occurring than
that of an ardent youth of St. Malo, who drank the health of
[Captain] Pontgravé with such persistent enthusiasm that he
fell overboard and was drowned." [23] Few characterizations of
New England's military potential during Queen Anne's War
are so graphically represented as in a momentary glimpse of
Maj. Benjamin Church, "the noted Indian fighter of King Philip's
War." He was at Tiverton, Rhode Island, when news of the
Deerfield massacre reached him. "Boiling with rage, he mounted
his horse and rode to Boston to propose a stroke of retaliation.
Church was energetic, impetuous, and bull-headed, sixty-five
years old, and grown so fat that when pushing through the
woods on the trail of Indians he kept a stout sergeant by him
to hoist him over fallen trees." [24] The comic theme recurs in describing an event of the winter of 1760, when the English garri-
son at Quebec had been forced to skirmish almost daily with
small bands of partisan French units around the countryside.
One such instance found the French behind defense works.
With a straight face Parkman related: "The [English] light
infantry advanced and poured in a brisk fire; on which the
French threw down their arms and fled. About eighty of them
were captured; but their commander, Herbin, escaped, leaving
to the victors his watch, hat and feather, wine, liquor-case, and
mistress. The English had six men wounded. . . ." [25]

New England Puritanism was not spared his satire, even
though Parkman treated it with the gentleness of an indulgent
and somewhat proud descendant. The short sixty-page section
called "The Feudal Chiefs of Acadia," added in 1893 to *The
Old Régime* and the last thing he wrote, is almost mischievous
in tone; although the action rambles and repeats, it reminds
one of a restrained, mock-heroic operetta. Two rival feudal
"barons" carried on a petty warfare and intrigue which eventu-

23. *Pioneers*, 2, 180.
24. *Half-Century*, 1, 121.
25. *M. and W.*, 3, 182.

ally involved pillage, wife stealing, and a complex series of
negotiations with Governor Winthrop and the original Brahman
class of Massachusetts. Medieval brutality and several scarcely
humorous pitched battles do not prevent the basic comedy of
the situation from setting the mood. In yet another instance
Parkman loosed his talent for satire on "Parson" Samuel Moody
of York, Maine, chaplain of the expedition to Louisbourg in
1745. At seventy he was something of a village tyrant, tough
and fanatical, with "lungs of brass, nerves of hammered iron,"
and sermons of equal endurance. At anyone so rash as to leave
Sunday meeting early he was apt to shout, "Come back, you
graceless sinner, come back!" When he sailed for Louisbourg,
"he took with him an axe, intended, as he said, to hew down
the altars of Antichrist and demolish his idols." [26]

What is undoubtedly the most humorous incident in the
series relates the escape of a band of fifty Jesuits and soldiers
from the camp of their Iroquois hosts one snowy evening in
1658. The French had learned that the Iroquois were treacher-
ously planning to fall upon and kill them. The problem lay in
leaving the camp without immediately inciting the Indians to
their malign purpose. As a solution someone proposed an "eat-
everything feast," which no tribe dared refuse if requested by
some person for whose spiritual benefit the feast was to be
given. By custom no one could stop eating until the honored
guest had given his permission. One of the Frenchmen requested, and was honored with, such a feast. Hours later, by
eleven o'clock, "the miserable [savages] were choking with
repletion." The Frenchman was still silent. "They bent to their
task again; but Nature soon reached her utmost limit, and they
sat helpless as a conventicle of gorged turkey buzzards." An
ally "played soft airs on a violin," and soon the entire tribe
dropped into sleep or coma; at which the band of Frenchmen
slipped away, seized the canoes, and fled across the lake
and on to the settlements, leaving the gathering of dull and

26. *Half-Century*, 2, 79–80.

stupefied Iroquois to discover in the morning the counter-treachery.[27]

But do heroes and their exploits account for New France? Parkman's most recent biographer has asserted that Parkman has provided a "Great Man" interpretation of history.[28] If true, it is hard to imagine that as a historian he could ever have exercised a permanent influence on a profession which has long since come to regard a Great Man interpretation as misleading. The issue calls for careful analysis.

It is fair to say that Parkman organized his series in terms of special considerations—among other things, literary and dramatic interest, and emphasis on certain qualities of character or action which he regarded as of particular merit and importance —and that these determined the structure but did not impair the validity of his history. Unfortunately some chapters in the series, taken by themselves, seem to have distorted the facts to achieve an effect. Such instances are rare and peripheral, but they will be noted. Aside from these passages the series does not seem to support a Great Man conclusion. For one thing lengthy attention to adventurous men does not of itself indicate a particular interpretation of historical causation. Parkman valued "character" in men for its own sake; nowhere did he imply that character was exclusively critical in determining events. Secondly, it can be shown that Parkman went beyond his treatment of men in erecting a full structure of historical events which does not primarily depend on identifying the men or what they did. The structure itself may not satisfy many modern historians, but such dissatisfaction is irrelevant to the question of Great Men.

Frequent incidents from Parkman's works might, at first glance, be called crucial in emphasizing the importance of an

27. *Old Régime*, 1, 90–94.
28. See Mason Wade, *Francis Parkman, Heroic Historian* (New York, 1942), p. 451, and Wade, *Journals*, p. xii.

individual decision. His interest in each of these events is understandable; they were the very stuff of drama, and each proved
a turning point in the history of New France. A few of the more
spectacular are worth discussing: Champlain's decision to skirmish with the Iroquois; the plans of La Salle which resulted
in his exploration of the Ohio and Illinois valleys; Frontenac's
role in the strengthening of Quebec; the decision of the Massachusetts government in 1745, carried by a single vote in the
General Court, to attack Louisbourg; the influence of Pitt in the
British government after 1758; the decision of an obscure French
militia captain, assigned the task of guarding the path up the
cliff of Quebec, to send most of his men home on the very day
preceding Wolfe's landing. Analysis of scattered incidents cannot prove a great deal; yet the evidence for those cited suggests
Parkman's general approach to historical causation.

First of all, what is said of Champlain? Although Parkman
admitted Champlain's decision to be *"in some measure* doubtless the cause of a long suite of murderous conflicts . . . to generations yet unborn,"[29] he also stated that "from first to last it
was the policy of France in America" to play politics with the
northern and western tribes for purposes of French expansion,
and that such a game was almost certain to result in Iroquois
hostility. In fact, alliance with any bloc of Indian tribes practically required that the French fight with them against their
enemies.[30] What Champlain accomplished or caused was almost
certain to have happened anyway. The same may be said for
La Salle's career, though on less specific evidence. If Parkman
had been a proponent of Great Man, his final eulogy of his hero
would surely have stated La Salle's importance in determining
history. But this magnificent appraisal of La Salle concerned
only his personal qualities and the innate weaknesses that had
led, after his successes, to his downfall.[31] In ten years almost

29. *Pioneers*, 2, 178. Italics mine.
30. *Ibid.*, pp. 112–13.
31. *La Salle*, pp. 431–2.

nothing remained to mark his career. The feeble colony on the Illinois made but a tiny contribution to the history of New France. La Salle succeeded where, had he failed, others would have tried.

As for Frontenac, Parkman explicitly suggested that, however heroic, his career was probably not crucial to the history of New France, and that he did not save it from as much danger as is thought.[32] From Parkman's account of New France it is also clear that many factors assured Frontenac's success: the presence of French regular troops (a decision made by Louis XIV), the timely prosperity of the fur trade, the feebleness of English aggression, and the skill and ability of the outpost garrisons in the West. The Massachusetts attack on Louisbourg is perhaps not a fair example, because its results were chiefly obliterated by a diplomatic decision in 1748, itself the product of multiple forces. The factor of a single vote may have determined the fate of the entire campaign,[33] but as long as no one can decide whose vote produces a one-vote majority it is difficult to see how an event determined by a vote could be subject to a Great Man interpretation. Any number of fortuitous occurrences at Louisbourg, furthermore, would have altered the outcome as positively as if the vote itself had not carried.

Parkman's effusion over Pitt's character and the effect he had on the war certainly partakes of the Great Man tradition.[34] But if the entire history of New France to 1758 meant anything, it was the virtual certainty that the British would have conquered Canada, later if not sooner. Parkman did not attribute the causes to Pitt. They stemmed from France, Germany, Austria, and America and centered in an infinite number of small decisions made by an infinite number of people. Likewise the significance of the Heights of Abraham was that the fate of North America did not hang on a brambled path and its

32. *Frontenac*, p. 459 and n.
33. See *Half-Century*, 2, 69.
34. *M. and W.*, 2, 246–52.

sentries. It is possible that Wolfe's expedition would have sailed home had the path been blocked, but this contingency depended as much on Wolfe's decision as on the actions of the French guard. The fortunes of New France, Parkman declared, hung on the precarious chances of September 12, not for all time, but for "a little longer." [35] The conclusion is obvious: to narrate one cause or decision is not to ignore other causes or decisions unless one declares the "one cause" to have been the only significant one, the only one that made valid history. Parkman's interest in the dramatic events of history was never so unbalanced as to ignore the importance of the undramatic events. He would have undoubtedly regarded as naïve the Great Man view which ascribes to a specific individual and his actions the *significant* cause for a train of consequences.

What is to be concluded about Parkman's men? The history of New France, of the conquest of the wilderness, and of the clash of colonial powers was to a large extent the history of the exploits of identifiable individuals, leaders in a social structure peculiarly stratified and peculiarly dependent on its leaders. Military exploits, a semifeudal and monarchical structure of government, a ruling priest class, colonizing schemes run on principles of absolute command lend themselves to treatment which stresses the decisions of leaders; the very nature of the sources (generally the records of literate leaders or their sympathizers) makes this treatment almost a necessity, if one is not to resort to speculation or unwarranted inference. Parkman's own interests and enthusiasms made his use of it even more likely. In one way or another these men were "representative men," either in their experiences or as symbols of certain characteristics of their times. Parkman's artistry in rendering their experiences is a valid historical technique for understanding the past. That he chose deliberately to emphasize the individuals does not mean that he could not have written in other terms. Where his sources were more comprehensive and less individu-

35. *Ibid.*, 3, 128.

alistic, as in the final two volumes, for example, he did not build his narrative so much on individuals as on nations, colonies, and groups of men.

In stressing the record of heroic leaders Parkman often subordinated background of an economic or institutional nature. A noteworthy instance was his emphasis on Laval, to the exclusion of other factors, in the history of New France from 1660 to 1680. At other times, such as in dealing with European backgrounds, he was apt to do violence to the logic of history, when, for example, he interpreted national policies in terms of the personal character or caprice of certain heads of state, at one point apparently relying on Carlyle for a summary of German history during the reign of Frederick the Great.[36] But for his story of New France the underlying institutional and economic factors are nearly always present, implicit when not explicit, sometimes only sketched in and reduced to essentials. Without them his structure would clearly collapse. A summary of his treatment of institutions and of the economic underpinnings to his history should dispel any doubts of his ability to comprehend them and should suggest that in no sense did he rely upon a Great Man framework.

INSTITUTIONAL AND ECONOMIC STRUCTURE

The strength and weakness of colonial policy and colonizing methods forms a basic element in the story of the New World. From the beginning some enterprises failed no matter what their leaders did. Witness the Huguenot settlement in Florida. It was planned as a military colony for a political party; its settlers could neither sustain themselves nor fulfill the conditions needed for success, a point which Parkman made clear in the story. He also recognized how small a body of knowledge

36. *Ibid.,* 3, 236. Also for general instances of this type, see *M. and W.,* chaps. 1, 18, 31.

had been built up to strengthen the chances for success.[37] It almost seems as though 16th-century colonies were destined to fail precisely because they came first. Similar problems plagued Port Royal, the enterprise of De Monts in Acadia in 1607:

> First of Europeans, they had assayed to found an agricultural colony in the New World. The leaders of the enterprise had acted less as merchants than as citizens; and the fur-trading monopoly, odious in itself, had been used as the instrument of a large and generous design. There was a radical defect, however, in their scheme of settlement. Excepting a few of the leaders, those engaged in it had not chosen a home in the wilderness of New France, but were mere hirelings, without wives or families, and careless of the welfare of the colony.[38]

Parkman likewise believed that all comparable French colonies were destined to fail when they did not contain a majority of volunteer settlers capable of establishing an economic basis for a colony. "No Mayflower," he wrote, "ever sailed from a port of France." [39] This remark, taken in its context, would lead one to suspect the author of having been a political, even economic, determinist.

Parkman's account of La Salle's disastrous colony in Texas likewise includes an analysis of the backgrounds for overseas enterprises in 17th-century France. A combination of circumstances, including an inaccurate map, an ignorance of Indian culture, an illusion over gold and silver, made certain a failure strongly indicated from the first. Spanish vessels and troops assured the defeat of any settlement that far south. The successor to La Salle's colony was the colony of Louisiana begun in 1697, an enterprise which repeated nearly every mistake in colonizing that France had ever made. Individuals wealthy

37. *Pioneers, 1,* 26, 34.
38. *Pioneers, 2,* 98.
39. *Pioneers, 1,* 35.

enough to initiate such ventures generally had to be given
virtual autonomy over them, and as a consequence considerations of personal profit often made it impossible for colonists
to thrive. Louisiana, founded as a royal project from fear of
English designs on the same territory, became a fiasco, and the
colony barely survived a later era. French colonial policy,
in fact, proved to be as responsible as any other single factor
for the ultimate loss of Canada. In 1758 the government
notified Vaudreuil and the colonial officials that Canada
would be abandoned to its fate. The exigencies of the European
war loomed larger in official eyes than the needs of an outpost
colony which for a generation had consumed vast wealth in
subsidies and had brought in a negligible return. One of the
chief reasons for supporting Canada so long was fear of English
conquest, and by 1758 the fear had all but become a reality.

The material foundations for the growth and history of New
France are carefully delineated in *The Old Régime,* of which
nearly two hundred pages, finished by 1874, may be considered
as one of the pioneer institutional studies in American scholarship. Much of this study is essential for an understanding of the
more dramatic narrative history. The two dominant features of
the French colonial economy were the prevailing mercantilist
concept of economic absolutism (i.e., regulation by decree to
promote monopoly profits accruing to the trading companies),
and the heavy dependence on France for subsidies. This dependence was due to the nature of the resources available to the
colony. Agriculture in a basic sense supported itself, yet, because there were no storage facilities, the grain surpluses every
autumn had to be sold at a loss on an immediate market. By
1660 England controlled most of the Atlantic coastal fishing
grounds. (Newfoundland fishing was usually carried on directly
from French ports.) Industry was negligible. The colony as a
result sank deeper into debt each year with no hope of recovery,
for imports from France sold under conditions of ruthless
monopoly and price fixing. All foreign trade was forbidden, and

the interests of officials and the larger companies constantly
superseded the trading rights of the smaller merchants.

The beaver trade was chaotic. Furs were the only product to
create a substantial revenue, and the livelihood of most of the
settlers depended on them; the trade could be cut off in an
instant by hostile Iroquois at the yearly portage down the Ottawa. Control of the trade rested theoretically in a government
monopoly, but in practice the swarm of individual trappers and
the illicit trade which the military outposts intercepted actually
forced a reasonable flow of revenue directly to the settlers.
Much of the history of Canadian politics became a continuous
squabble over the rake-off from the system of fur trade, and
the course of westward expansion was mostly determined by
the fact that the trade required the wilderness, the Indian, and
a military organization to keep it secure from English rivals.

The accession of Louis XIV and his support of Colbert's policies brought about a far-reaching evolution in the structure of
colonial government. Colbert proceeded to eliminate the old
feudal autonomy and to substitute direct royal paternalism. The
feudal structure became essentially a system of land distribution
and tenure. The seigneur now possessed little power in his own
right, and farmer and seigneur alike lived under an absolute
state. In theory the colonial government was to be kept weak
and subservient to Versailles, for the king wished to rule colonists directly. In practice the colonial authorities exercised real
and substantial power. Decrees directed every phase of life,
though many of them were ignored. Irreverence, whether to
church, king, or God, was brutally dealt with. The population
lived in an intellectual vacuum; learning, information, and
knowledge were the monopoly of the priest and official. "It is of
very great consequence that the people should not be left at
liberty to speak their minds," wrote an intendant, whose position became that of an official spy on the governor.[40] In the matter of a population policy the French government was remark-

40. *Old Régime, 2*, 79.

ably aggressive. Its encouragement of immigration ultimately failed (Parkman says fatally so); but subsidies for children helped to double the population every twenty years for a century, which is now considered to have been one of the highest continuous rates of human increase ever recorded. Despite this phenomenon, French Canada in 1760 had but 75,000 inhabitants, scarcely one-twentieth of the English population in the seaboard colonies.

Parkman's singular gift for re-creating a scene extended to his characterization of the people themselves. Though his sources were fragmentary and not always reliable, they remain even today probably the best that exist. New France was an unruly, colonial frontier land, where, in a thin belt along three hundred miles of the banks of the St. Lawrence, a meager population strove to build a life in the sultry summer heat and in the miserable Canadian winters. The wilderness had been pushed back no more than a few miles from the river. Disbanded soldiers, fur trappers, Indians, and outlaws roamed everywhere; life was precarious, the law unenforceable, the people more a product of their newer environment than of their national origins. Though Parkman seems to have possessed a Brahmanian reluctance to concern himself with lower-class individuals, he was quite capable of discussing them as a group. The backbone of the colonial military and forest-ranging forces was the undisciplined, roving, free-lance *habitant,* often of noble birth, often of the French peasantry, but in Canada risen to become a free farmer or soldier. Parkman also occasionally discussed characteristics of race and nationality, a disquieting habit that needs further consideration. One of his views seems to have been that the French colonists proved incapable of freedom, self-discipline, or self-reliance—in short, they were not New Englanders.

Parkman properly confined his treatment of the English colonies to providing necessary background for English-French relations. His readers are led to believe, whether correctly or not, that these relations were confined almost entirely to military struggles, and although the *course* of struggle was never certain, the two colonies were destined to conflict and the French to lose. The English were usually aroused to action only after incessant border raids had driven them to a pitch of fury and after the two nations had begun their conflicts in Europe. Parkman's enthusiasm for New England's secular virtues did not prevent him from ridiculing the amateur militarism of untrained farmers. The ill-fated, quixotic gallantry of the Massachusetts militia and navy in threatening Quebec with attack in 1690 contrasts almost comically with the epic invasion of 1759. The closing remarks on the expedition reveal only disdain for martial incompetence: "Massachusetts had made her usual mistake. She had confidently believed that ignorance and inexperience could match the skill of a tried veteran, and that the rude courage of her fishermen and farmers could triumph without discipline or leadership. The conditions of her material prosperity were adverse to efficiency in war. A trading republic, without trained officers, may win victories; but it wins them either by accident or by an extravagant outlay in money and life." [41]

For over half a century Massachusetts settlers tried nothing quite so harebrained. Then in 1745 occurred their invasion of Cape Breton Island, one of the major episodes in Parkman's works and brilliantly written. Offering few details of an economic nature or of basic campaign problems such as supply, medical care, or finances, he paid special attention to the institutional problem of leadership and the politics of command. In his glimpses of the men involved, their moods and their reactions to war, his touches of satire convey the sense of confusion and the instances of humor without any loss of impact. Supporting the French were geography, fortifications, and experience. Against them the New Englanders brought mostly determination and the ingenuity to capitalize on every turn of fortune. Whenever Parkman turned to the business at hand, reporting

41. *Frontenac*, p. 285.

with objective impersonality the vivid human highlights of a campaign, he intruded nothing of his own except the experience of action. His facts and his extraneous moral theories were rigidly separated.

Ten years later, when the colonies faced a major military threat, they met it somewhat better prepared. Despite Parkman's insistence on the superior moral fiber of the New Englander, as contrasted to colonists farther south, his facts led him to attribute the valor and courage of their militia in part to geographical position: they had been trained to war for three generations; their lands and houses had been raided and burned, and their citizens, from sheer necessity and not moral virtue, were far more ready than those in the other colonies to vote funds for defense. In the course of war the colonies and the British officials alike developed techniques of action that contributed heavily to victory. The war was won, however, by the British fleet and the British army, employing standard European tactics. Parkman also acknowledged the permanent impact on colonial institutions of the presence and ideas of British regulars. But by then the story of New France had ended, and since his was not a history of the English, not even of New England, he elaborated their problems no further.

Parkman's presentation of English colonial backgrounds, though limited, was carefully worked out, remaining faithful to the logic of events. One cannot say the same for the background glimpses he offered of Europe. On occasion he failed to provide vital facts and developments which the reader is entitled to know. At other times he seemed to have substituted for careful analysis a sweeping glance at kings, mistresses, and court pageantry. His sources for such glimpses may explain much, for they included secondary accounts and extracts from the European tradition of romantic history. As background for the Huguenot colony, for example, Parkman set forth an account of intrigue between court, church, army, and nobility unnecessarily prolonged for its value as color rather than as background, and, unfortunately, too far removed from his most reliable checkrein, his experience.[42] In another instance the reader is informed that Louis XIV, upon learning of the desperate plight of his infant colony in Texas, refused to send further aid or help, or even a ship for escape.[43] A new policy? Rivalry at court? Royal boredom with the problems of colonies? Parkman made no attempt to supply an answer, and the incident is left hanging. In 1756 the French had formed a sudden coalition with Austria against Prussia. "Frederick the Great had drawn upon himself an avalanche. Three women—two empresses and a concubine —controlled the forces of the three great nations, Austria, Russia, and France; and they all hated him." [44] Why? Because of personal pique and wounded female vanity. Therefore, the reader is led to understand, Europe plunged into war. Glibness of this sort does not really damage the structure of Parkman's main story. But as background material for New France it would have been better omitted. The passage as it stands may be accurate in itself, yet its romantic verbiage only obscures the more important underlying facts. Even worse was Parkman's treatment of the Duke of Newcastle, George II's First Lord of the Treasury in 1754, a politician whom he evidently disliked. He could think of nothing better, apparently, than to quote long passages from Horace Walpole's memoirs of the reign of George II, describing Newcastle as only Walpole could.[45] Since the excerpts stand alone, one can only surmise that Parkman accepted Walpole's judgment for his own. They are entertaining, but Parkman's uncritical use of them seems no less than fatuous compared with the rigorous historical methods which underlie the rest of his work.

Parkman's value judgments on peoples and nations betray a

42. *Pioneers, 1,* 21–8, 101.
43. *La Salle,* p. 463.
44. *M. and W.,* 2, 39 ff.
45. *Ibid., 1,* 184–7.

weakness of a rather different sort. They involve, on the whole, assumptions of a biological nature, understandable enough when he made them, but most of which are no longer tenable. To accuse him, as one critic has, of Anglo-Saxon chauvinism is probably as irrelevant as to accuse Franklin of having believed in Newtonian physics.[46] Were Parkman writing today, though he might still retain his faith in nationalism and in the superior virtues of masculinity, his views on race and heredity would be possibly no less advanced for our times than were his actual views for his own. But read today as he wrote them they constitute an undeniable anachronism in a history otherwise remarkably free from historical fashions. Among his many pontifical judgments were these: certain peoples are fit for freedom and others are not; habits of thought and reason and qualities of character are inherited (the Acadian farmers are "enfeebled by hereditary mental subjection"); racial strains determine political qualities ("The Germanic race, and especially the Anglo-Saxon branch of it, is peculiarly masculine, and, therefore, peculiarly fitted for self-government"); economic self-reliance, scorning the aid of government, is a necessary condition for political growth and prosperity; colonial Virginian society was stratified into classes of slaves, poor whites ("boisterous," "vicious," "of low origin"), farmers ("good English stock"), and great landowners ("well-born," "high-spirited," "indolent," "vigorous"); Pennsylvania Germans are "dull, ignorant," the Irish are "quarrelling," the Scots "vigorous"; the New Englanders are "a masculine race . . . the sinews . . . hardened at the expense of blood and flesh—and this literally as well as figuratively." Various other judgments, many of them anticipating Social Darwinism, fortified these predilections. "The fittest," for Parkman, were generally those most fit to survive in the wilderness. Of the Ottawa Indians under Pontiac he noted gratuitously, "The law of the survival of the fittest had wrought

46. C. W. Alvord, "Francis Parkman," *The Nation, 117* (October 10, 1923), 395.

on this heterogeneous crew through countless generations; and
with the primitive Indian, the fittest was the hardiest, fiercest,
most adroit, and most wily." To explain "the hardy Canadian
race of bush-rangers" he speculated that their early family life
in winter was so rugged that "the weaker sort died, the strong
survived." Such fallacies were common assumptions in the late
19th century. Time has weeded out most of them. Within the
structure of Parkman's history they usually occupy harmless
nooks and corners where they cause little damage.[47]

In characterizing Parkman's historical structure, I would say
in conclusion that with a minimum of distortion he arranged the
evidence in order to emphasize those episodes most possessed
of drama and color and the exploits of vigorous men. Despite
his preference for heroism—in Jesuits, in warriors, in Indians,
in leaders—he did not slight the less personal factors of political
and economic significance. No matter what his preferences, his
histories probably would have achieved lasting success, for
it seems to me that the qualities which keep Parkman's work
alive today, in contrast to the histories of Prescott, for example,
lie outside the choice of subject or the emphasis of interpretation. Parkman's achievement lives, because to the large and
permanent themes which he found in history he added a quality
from his own experience that enables the reader in turn to experience them. This quality lay at the root of his artistry, and it
needs separate consideration.

47. See, variously, *Old Régime*, 2, 198–202; *M. and W.*, 1, 19–
38, 217, 269; 2, 39.

CHAPTER THREE

The Re-creation of History

It is the habit of certain minds to give an all-
excluding fulness to the object, the thought, the
word they alight upon, and to make that for the
time the deputy of the world.
        —RALPH WALDO EMERSON, "Art," *Essays:*
        First Series

HISTORY AS VISUAL EXPERIENCE

IN HIS preface to *The Jesuits* Parkman stated that his care in
writing history was "to secure the greatest possible accuracy
of statement, and to reproduce an image of the past with photographic clearness and truth." Allusions to visual sense and metaphors that invoke light, appearance, or seeing occur continually
through his books. His most compelling writing, in fact, literally
describes; at the same time it is seldom static. "The narrator
must seek to imbue himself with the life and spirit of the times.
He must study events in their bearings near and remote; in the
character, manner, and habits of those who took part in them.
He must himself be, as it were, a sharer or a spectator of the
action he describes." [1]

Parkman rendered movement and action in words of force
and elemental simplicity. He stripped his style of phrases that
intellectualize or that tend to obstruct one's direct experiencing

1. *Pioneers, 1,* c. Italics are mine.

of what he wished to show. Consequently his style enables his own apprehension of the experience to become that of his readers, who thereby share in the event to the extent which he did. Even in expository prose, analyzing or summarizing, his imagery tends to reduce itself to a universal frame of reference, of things seen, felt, or thought which are common to a wide class of readers. To talk of a distinction between intellect and sensation is precarious, since the two are ultimately inseparable, but it may clarify the nature of Parkman's prose to suggest that in countless instances it renders the complex issues of a historical trend, normally understood as abstractions and concepts which make sense only through intellectual effort, in terms of sensations rather than in terms exclusively intellectual. If as a result his writing loses in accuracy and qualification, if it occasionally tends dangerously toward generalization, it nevertheless gains immense force and swiftness of movement. It enabled him to convey a broad movement of history in brief, tangible images which express what he saw to have been the essential character of the past. The reader experiences its character from the image, even while he grasps it with his mind. As long as he may rely on Parkman's abilty to comprehend what actually did occur, he finds in the image a quality of truth, conveyed to him as a visual experience.

The simplest visual experience occurs in Parkman's panoramas. The scenes so described are generally based on original documents, but in the process of rendering them Parkman relied mostly on his own direct observations, and the wording was his own. A panorama suggests movement or unfolding, and this was precisely his technique of presentation. The wilderness changes and slips slowly by as the reader moves through it. The account of the Mississippi written by Joliet and Marquette was the first of an infinite series of descriptions of that river to occur in literature, and Parkman presents it with the authenticity of his own vision. They

glided through an endless growth of wild rice. . . . On
either hand rolled the prairie, dotted with groves and trees
. . . thickets and marshes and broad bare sand-bars. . . .
In the morning the mist hung on the river like a bridal veil,
then melted before the sun. . . . A torrent of yellow mud
rushed furiously athwart the calm blue current of the Mississippi, boiling and surging and sweeping in its course logs,
branches, and uprooted trees. They had reached the mouth
of the Missouri. . . . The sun glowed through the hazy air
with a languid stifling heat. . . .[2]

This hazardous adventure included hunting, exploring, Indian
feasts, and disease, and ultimately resulted in death for one of
the two men; action and scenic movement alternate, and one
catches in both the elemental exploits of men facing a wilderness.

In another instance the reader stands on the south shore of
the Lower St. Lawrence in the late autumn of the 1680's.

A ship from France, the last of the season, holds her way for
Quebec. . . . Swelling her patched and dingy sails, she
glides through the wilderness and the solitude where there
is nothing but her to remind you of the great troubled world
behind and the little troubled world before. On the far
verge of the ocean-like river clouds and mountains mingle
in dim confusion. Fresh gusts from the north dash waves
against the ledges, sweep through the quivering spires of
stiff and stunted fir-trees. . . .[3]

A local French curé rounds a point in his tiny canoe; he is on
a trip through his parish, which extends sixty miles in a thin
strip along the river bank. The reader follows the curé and is
made aware, as if having followed him for a year, of the life he
lives and the things he sees.

2. *La Salle,* pp. 61–70.
3. *Old Régime,* 2, 141–2.

Or again, Parkman places the reader on an incoming ship and gives him the sensations of a new settler. Passing Quebec he moves up the river to Montreal and slowly down again as the narrator points out to him what is virtually the entire colony of New France (1670), the houses, feudal farms, cabins, huts, forests, and docks. Parkman made of this view of Quebec from a slowly approaching vessel a leitmotiv that binds together a century and a half of drama. The reader sees what Champlain first saw; later, the view from Phips' fleet off the rock, in 1690. One may follow various governors—Tracy, Frontenac, Montcalm—as they disembark from France and climb, "breathing heavily," the long steep path to the Upper Town, their new home. Finally one arrives with Wolfe in 1759 and stares at the same natural wonder, noting this time the redoubts, entrenchments, and especially the sheer impregnability of the cliff walls. Yet the cliff was breached, and Quebec, wracked for weeks by naval cannon, battered by invasion in its final hours, fell to the English; one enters the town with them and moves through its streets. In another few weeks only the occupation troops and civilian inhabitants remain.

The fleet was gone; the great river was left a solitude; and the chill days of a fitful November passed over Quebec in alternations of rain and frost, sunshine and snow. . . . The Lower Town was a wilderness of scorched and crumbling walls. . . . On the right was a skeleton of tottering masonry, and the buildings on the left were a mass of ruin, where ragged boys were playing at see-saw among the fallen planks and timbers. . . . The Cathedral was burned to a shell. . . . The bombshells that fell through the roof had broken into the pavement, and as they burst had thrown up the bones and skulls of the dead from the graves beneath.[4]

4. *M. and W.*, 3, pp. 172–3. Parkman's footnotes indicate that the details of his description are authentic, taken from paintings and letters.

If there is any quality of visual truth which renders history timeless it is the impact of such a scene on those who have recently stood in the market square of Caen or by the river in Liège or in any nameless town on the Rhine, the Dnieper, the Vistula, or the Po. Ragged boys were playing seesaw in Babylon and Rome and will continue their game long after men have ceased turning their cities into wildernesses.

There are a score of other scenes through which Parkman conducts his reader: the coast line of Louisbourg and the islands off the Acadian peninsula, the wilderness west of Fort Cumberland when Braddock's army cut its way through, the Black Hills and the Platte River Valley, as backdrop for the expedition of La Vérendrye in the 1740's, but seen and described and preserved by Parkman in his own notebook a century later. Perhaps the most striking panorama of all is of an aerial flight over the wilderness battleground from Albany to Montreal. A prelude to the final years of the war it combines ingeniously a sense of over-all geography with the reality of a specific scene. The reader moves with a flock of wild fowl north in the spring, and the land moves under him "like a map"; frontier posts along the Hudson, the "geometric lines of Fort Edward"; then "the lake stretched northward, like some broad river, trenched between mountain ranges still leafless and gray. . . . Ticonderoga, with the flag of the Bourbons, like a flickering white speck, waving on its ramparts. . . . On the left the mountain wilderness of the Adirondacks, like a stormy sea congealed." [5] The land slips beneath in utter solitude, and one feels detached from it even while caught up in it. Parkman's eye and controlled imagination served him so well that today one could scarcely improve the authenticity of his aerial perspective.

One finds a second and more difficult type of "visual" characterization in some of Parkman's expository writing. A broad historical movement is reduced to graphic terms, metaphorically

5. *Ibid.*, 2, 140–1.

or through the medium of human symbols, not because he sought to render history more accurate thereby but because such sketches afford glimpses of the structural background to more important or immediate matters; full, qualified accuracy would have made them interminable. Parkman's flair for imagery often enabled him to suggest the essential core of an idea where an analytical treatise would have put one no closer to it. One may dislike having to trust so absolutely a historian's ability to generalize, and I have already shown how far off the track Parkman occasionally strayed. But in matters where he had made himself expert his general conclusions have gone unchallenged; in any event his conclusion would be irrelevant in appraising his technique of visual characterization.

Consider, for example, this passage: "It was the nature of French colonization to seize upon detached strategic points, and hold them by the bayonet, forming no agricultural basis, but attracting the Indians by trade, and holding them by conversion. A musket, a rosary, and a pack of beaver skins may serve to represent it, and in fact it consisted of little else." [6] In the first sentence five active verbs, balanced in two parts, establish a vision of military movement. Here the verbs require people as their subjects: the action is made personal because the reader "sees" people in action. The action, however, is reported impersonally and objectively, for the sentence focuses on "colonization," and its function is to contrast French colonization with what had been said about English colonization in a preceding paragraph. Parkman reduced nearly every element in this exposition to simple terms: point, bayonet, conversion, trade. One's understanding is further reinforced by his use of emblematic objects, which reduces to even simpler terms the "nature" of colonization. Yet in reduction one has not lost a sense of details, for the emblems stand not only for what they mean to us—and this is graphic enough—but for what has preceded them in the story.

6. *Frontenac*, p. 395.

Earlier in the series Parkman attempted a complex comparison of French and Canadian feudalism to show how the latter evolved from the former. In France the older feudal lords had gradually lost their power to the central monarchy. This plainly involved administrative and local political problems, for power must reside in people who deal with such problems, and power does not simply "change" without reference to people. Parkman described it in terms of the key person, the intendant, whom, in characterizing, he made use of to suggest the nature and quality of the change in government.

He was the King's agent; of modest birth, springing from the legal class; owing his present to the King, and dependent on him for his future; learned in the law and trained to administration. It was by such instruments that the powerful centralization of the monarchy enforced itself throughout the kingdom, and, penetrating beneath the crust of old prescriptions, supplanted without seeming to supplant them. The courtier noble looked down in the pride of rank on the busy man in black at his side; but this man in black, with the troop of officials at his beck, controlled finance, the royal courts, public works, and all the administrative business of the province.[7]

A visual experience conveys the entire nature of an institutional evolution.

To be sure Parkman often overpainted; in his desire to savor every ounce of romance in these vast historic movements he sometimes lapsed into the empty rhetoric of mid-century oratory: "Years rolled on. France [in 1543], long tossed among the surges of civil commotion, plunged at last into a gulf of fratricidal war. Blazing hamlets, sacked cities, fields streaming with slaughter, profaned altars, and ravished maidens, marked the track of the tornado."[8] Almost as florid was his reflection upon

7. *Old Régime*, 2, 62–3.
8. *Pioneers*, 2, 51.

Pitt's coming to head the king's government: "As Nature, languishing in chill vapors and dull smothering fogs, revives at the touch of the sun, so did England spring into fresh life under the kindling influence of one great man." [9] Much of his earlier style defeats itself in a plethora of "sullen," "gloomy," "groaning," "solemn," "sluggish," "portentous"—all to characterize natural phenomena. But in his last two books he pared his phrases to the bone, and his words seem to hit with the impact of their original freshness.

"He must be a sharer or a spectator of the action he describes," Parkman wrote of the historian. One finds yet another, and most dramatic, type of visual characterization in the many accounts of small border raids and partisan exploits of small bands of men in the wilderness. I have noted Parkman's intense, lifelong enthusiasm for such adventures, and how authentically he could feel himself a part of them. Not only had he experienced the wilderness environment; his own temperament seemed to reflect the feelings and moods of the men who took part in them. What the records did not reveal he could supply. The re-creation of these exploits may well be considered the most convincing and permanent of his writings.

The striking element in them is the presence of the wilderness. It pervades every action. The miseries of weather and warfare occur in any military campaign, and will likewise appear in military histories. To the weather and the savagery Parkman added a greater note of drama: the struggle between man and an indifferent wilderness. Whenever men stepped off the edge of society and hacked a trail through the swamps, rocks, and windfalls they committed every nerve and sense to the elemental act of survival. To fail to move, to fail to act, was to lose ground. Only a few ever expected to make their living in the wilderness; the Indians did and the trappers did, but for the rest (including Parkman) the wilderness was a foreign environ-

9. *M. and W.*, 2, 252.

ment in which to transact one's business or pleasure and get out.
Man struggled to destroy it, to tame it, to enjoy it, as the case
warranted. The stumbling forms of men whom Parkman in his
imagination accompanied on their exploits did not adapt themselves permanently to the forest; they moved through it because
to accomplish their purpose they could not avoid doing so. The
wilderness formed a backdrop and a set of conditions imposed
on those who waged border warfare. Describe the backdrop,
convey the actual impact of elemental conditions, and the warfare becomes real. Parkman's style functioned not to recapture
the subjective moods of other men but to re-create the all-
coercive sensations of weather, forest, color, and movement,
adding to them the dimension of personal experience. So well
did he succeed that his readers, sensing the wilderness firsthand,
move along with the men and react as they did.

A simple illustration of Parkman's re-creation may be had by
comparing one of his descriptive paragraphs with that part of
the original document on which the description is based. The
annual report of Jesuit missionary activities for the year 1639
contained a firsthand account of the winter trip of two priests,
Garnier and Jogues, through the forest to the Erie villages:

> In the middle of the journey, being unable to find a certain
> detour which would have led us to some cabins which are a
> little isolated, we were overtaken by night in a fir grove;
> we were in a damp place and could not find a drier one; we
> had great difficulty gathering a few pieces of wood to make
> a little fire, and a few dry branches for us to lie upon; the
> snow was threatening to put out our fire, but it ceased sud-
> denly. God be praised, we passed the night very well.[10]

From this bare account Parkman built the following picture.

10. Excerpt from *Rélation . . . des Hurons*, chap. 10, as reported
and sent by Lalement to Vimont, May 27, 1640. (P. 95, Quebec ed.,
A. Coté, 1858, to which Parkman had access.) The above is a transla-
tion literally rendered from the French of the Quebec edition.

The forests were full of snow; and the soft, moist flakes were still falling thickly, obscuring the air, beplastering the gray trunks, weighing to the earth the boughs of spruce and pine, and hiding every footprint of the narrow path. The Fathers missed their way, and toiled on till night, shaking down at every step from the burdened branches a shower of fleecy white on their black cassocks. Night overtook them in a spruce swamp. Here they made a fire with great difficulty, cut the evergreen boughs, piled them for a bed, and lay down. The storm presently ceased; and, "praised be God," writes one of the travelers, "we passed a very good night." [11]

Implicit in Parkman's rendering of the Jesuits' account was the historian's assumption of the continuity of experience. His imagination supplied the document with details that are valid in experience; and these details, completely consistent with the known facts, bring the reader closer to the event than does the original document. Parkman's version is not only truthful; it is memorably pictorial. Its qualities of color and mood transcend the facts to present an artistically valid version of the facts. It is history re-created.

A more sweeping scene of action enabled Parkman to employ a more complex visual technique. In the dead of winter, 1666, a war party of five hundred Frenchmen moved out over the "solid floor" of the St. Lawrence highway to attack the Dutch outpost of Schenectady. Their "snowshoes tied at their backs, [they] walked with difficulty and toil over the bare and slippery ice. A keen wind swept the river, and the fierce cold gnawed them to the bone. . . . Some fell in torpor and were dragged on by their comrades to the shivering bivouac." Here is a near view. But the scenes now alternate between a vast panorama and the detailed close-up, giving, as in a film, the dual awareness both of the event and of the men.

11. *Jesuits, 1,* 232. Parkman specifically mentions his source in a footnote.

Lake Champlain lay glaring in the winter sun, a sheet of spotless snow; and the wavy ridges of the Adirondacks bordered the dazzling landscape with the cold gray of their denuded forests. The long procession of weary men crept slowly on under the lee of the shore; and when night came they bivouacked by squads among the trees, dug away the snow with their snow-shoes, piled it in a bank around them, built their fire in the middle, and crouched about it on beds of spruce or hemlock—while, as they lay close packed for mutual warmth, the winter sky arched them like a vault of burnished steel, sparkling with the cold diamond lustre of its myriads of stars.[12]

The visual immediacy places the reader among the men. In seeing them simultaneously from a distance one maintains an objective detachment. The mood of the men is reflected by the impact of the wilderness on them. And all the while one is aware of the impersonal and awful vastness of the scene itself. Though the scenic description is from Parkman's own experience, the record of camping was a historical fact. To it Parkman added a quality of art which lifts both scene and event into a universal experience, suggestive of the qualities in history which he valued most.

In numerous other incidents the numbing terror of winter seems to sweep through the reader. One example is the account of the raid on Deerfield in 1704 and the subsequent fate of the prisoners. Such incidents comprised only a few out of hundreds which frontier settlers endured year by year for a generation. Parkman described the winter trek, three hundred miles to Montreal, in terse, subdued prose, relentless in pace. The terrible realism of the scene conveys a wintry horror all its own, drawing its power less from descriptive virtuosity than from a tension between word and event. The reader is told less than the facts but immediately perceives more.

12. *Old Régime, 1,* 247–8.

They came soon after to Green River, a stream then about knee-deep, and so swift that the water had not frozen. After wading it with difficulty, they climbed a snow-covered hill beyond. The minister, with strength almost spent, was permitted to rest a few moments at the top; and as the other prisoners passed by in turn, he questioned each for news of his wife. He was not left long in suspense. She had fallen from weakness in fording the stream, but gained her feet again, and, drenched in the icy current, struggled to the farther bank, when the savage who owned her, finding that she could not climb the hill, killed her with one stroke of his hatchet. Her body was left on the snow. . . .[13]

The details are presented stripped bare. Implicit in the prose is the impact of those same details as they are told to the minister. The serene detachment of the words establishes the minuteness of the incident amid a large sweep of time. But the incident engulfs the reader's sensations, for an instant completely involved in the shock and the tension. Events strange and remote, microscopic details of history, suddenly loom larger than life. Parkman has transfixed in one event part of the history of the New England border.

Other scenes reveal similar qualities. The midwinter attack on Grand Pré: a body of English occupation troops asleep in dry rooms, while sixty miles through the Acadian forest amid a white-swirling blizzard moved a band of young French partisans, "galants" and adventurers. Parkman clearly approved of them and admired their courage and military dash. The fight was bloody, the snow hampered movement, but when the surprised English surrendered, the two sides mingled (the officers did) in feasting and drinking while the snow continued to fall outside.[14] Compared with these tales the fabulous exploits of Rogers and his Rangers are often overwritten. The details of

13. *Half-Century, 1,* 72–3. The chief source for this was the diary of the minister.
14. *Half-Century, 2,* 183–200.

fighting, raiding, and prisoner catching somehow dilute the immediacy and the visual identification displayed better elsewhere. The account of Rogers' defeat in 1758 in a winter ambush, nevertheless, is a masterful description of partisan warfare, and the subsequent story of the band lost in the forest with a delirious guide assumes significance and atmosphere of peculiar intensity.[15] With careful objectivity Parkman suppressed all extraneous "subjective" speculation of whatever kind, though he permitted details from his own experience to fill out the structure. The fidelity of such accounts is the fidelity of documentary sources. The quality of visual "experiencing" is Parkman's.

One finds scattered through the history a few small incidents of unmistakably symbolic quality. They often center in some particular image or emblem, such as the cliffs of Quebec already mentioned. Their combined import suggests an awareness of the insignificance of men's efforts face to face with a wilderness which they have the audacity to proclaim as their own. It is by no means certain that Parkman determined in advance to present such a thread of poetic symbolism. Yet when the individual situations suggested themselves he was perceptive enough to grasp their deeper possibilities. One instance occurs in the first book of the series. By 1620 Quebec had been well settled as a military and trading post and a mission. There was only one agriculturally minded settler, a man named Hébert, who, with his wife, cultivated a vegetable garden. Years passed. The colony grew, trade prospered, Champlain envisaged an empire. But the brief invasion of an English fleet toppled the structure. The colony virtually disappeared, until, in 1632, Champlain returned with his men and found—"the stone cottage of the Héberts, surrounded with its vegetable gardens— the only thrifty spot amid a scene of neglect." [16] In a later book,

15. *M. and W.*, 2, 216–19.
16. *Pioneers*, 2, 276.

Parkman subtly needled the pretensions of the political animal
when faced with an empty continent. The minions of His Most
Christian Majesty paddled down the Ohio in 1749 and, in the
presence of the astonished Indians who lived there, buried
leaden plates in the soil, spoke before savage council fires, and
departed having hoped thereby to prevent the English (or even
the Indians) from seizing the land from its rightful owner.[17]
The most ironic scene of this nature depicts La Salle's party at
the mouth of the Mississippi. "The broad bosom of the great
Gulf opened on his sight, tossing its restless billows, limitless,
voiceless, lonely as when born of chaos, without a sail, without
a sign of life." They prepared a large pole bearing the arms and
title of Louis the Great. While the Indians of the party looked
on, the French chanted a *Te Deum* and La Salle proclaimed
possession of the river. The pole, a leaden plate, and a cross
were planted on the sandy marshland. Renewed shouts and
praises rang from their throats. Parkman added, "On that day
the realm of France received on parchment a stupendous accession. The fertile plains of Texas; the vast basin of the Mississippi
. . . a region of savannas and forests, sun-cracked deserts, and
grassy prairies, watered by a thousand rivers, ranged by a
thousand war-like tribes, passed beneath the sceptre of the
Sultan of Versailles; and all by the virtue of a feeble human
voice, inaudible at half a mile." [18] Here is surely the essence
of the dual focus in Parkman's writing—the vast panorama and
the individual exploit; the one is a permanent feature, impersonal, meaningless; the other insignificantly tiny, personalized,
yet the raw material of history. La Salle looms larger than any
other figure in Parkman's works, and the scene at the river's
mouth climaxes his career. But with superb irony Parkman contrasts the permanence of things with the feebleness of individuals, as if to say that for all of man's recorded exploits he makes
no history by himself, and that one obtains little understanding

17. *M. and W., 1*, 46–58.
18. *La Salle*, pp. 306–8.

of historical events except as one focuses his vision on the deeds, acts, and surroundings of men and not on the men themselves. In just these terms Parkman's artistry has made history and its meanings "real" for his readers.

SYNTHESIS IN MILITARY CONFLICT

The downfall of New France was the story which Parkman had originally set out to tell when his "theme" had first come to him at Harvard College. What fascinated him was the physical con-flict—the campaigns, the battles, the forts, the heroism and the folly of command, and the valor of men fighting. Van Wyck Brooks writes that Parkman was made for military action and knew it, and that, if he could not live it, to write of it was the one substitute left him.[19] His histories suggest that this was so. Conflict between two powers for colonial and commercial su-premacy interested him primarily in terms of military action. The economic factors, the "character" or moral state of the people, their administrative and political systems were impor-tant chiefly as they affected the ability of the two contestants to wage war. Having finished the account of New France under Frontenac, he was ready to write the military history of two colonial peoples in time of war. As in his previous works he did not permit essentially nondramatic, abstract details to clut-ter the field of action. The title of the crowning volume, one might expect, offers the two most dramatically satisfactory mili-tary commanders as symbols and representatives of a conflict that far transcended them. The nonmilitary events, like gaudy but disreputable camp followers, tag on behind the course of campaigns to provide sensuous relief between battles. I have suggested that Parkman was not blind to the importance of non-military events. He was fully aware of the basic nature of the

19. Van Wyck Brooks, *New England Indian Summer* (New York, 1940), p. 169.

international conflict; in final prefaces, introductory chapters, and concluding chapters, while slighting some factors, he placed the battles in their rightful perspective in the contest for world power. Having dispensed with that, he was prepared to re-create on his own terms the drama and experience of military action. Battles and campaigns climax his history.

The ultimate fate of New France could not have been resolved except by conflict. The colonial authority, internally corrupt and decaying from the brazen frauds of Bigot's political machine, was able to field a formidable military force, skillfully led and only feebly opposed. In the summer of 1757 New France reached its crest of military power. French forts still commanded the western forests, and their troops had won over the Indians by their brilliant success at Monongahela. Oswego had fallen (Parkman calls it the greatest French victory in America), the Lakes were secured, and Montcalm's men had razed Fort William Henry, neutralizing Lake George and strengthening Ticonderoga. A British fleet had been wrecked off Louisbourg, now reinforced by three French squadrons. New France won temporary security. But unfortunately the issue was to be decided at Versailles and not Quebec. Little by little, while the impetus of Pitt's leadership on British strategy sent British regulars moving across to the colonies, Montcalm's position began to crumble from under him. The support for his strength was drying up; Canada was left to its own resources, and by the day Wolfe's fleet had appeared around the Point of Orleans before Quebec its outer frontier had caved in as much from internal weakness as from British military power. The rest was a matter of time.

The historian who wishes to combine dramatic human action in agreeable settings with ruthless accuracy of place and time can hardly do better than narrate the operations of a military campaign. Not only is he apt to find useful a plethora of recorded statement, opinion, inference, and reminiscence, but military source material by its very nature offers to view the concrete

and material fact. The historian can talk of orders given and received, of men moving or running, and where they were and
how many of them. He can talk of cannon, fields of fire, lines of
regulars, flanks of provincials, columns of so many abreast, fire
power, and terrain. He can view the battlefield and pace off the
earthworks (often, not always; today the scene of Braddock's
defeat, for example, is a square mile of city blocks and rail-
roads). He can even attempt to "read" the military mind, for it
has fed on fare rigidly standardized and documented, and it is
taught to react in fairly predictable patterns. He can assess
merit and blame in terms of well-defined standards, for the
records are certain to include some information as to the tactical
conduct of units of men. Above all he can expect to render the
totality of the action with a maximum evocation of visual experience; the weather, the land forms, and the physical sensations
of men in battle are probably more easily recovered than any
other class of factors. The military historian is in one sense the
engineer among historians.

After he has reconstructed the factual totality he may choose
several alternate courses. If he is a literary or dramatic historian
he may wish to communicate some sense of how men felt or
thought; if he had been Parkman he would have noted evidences
of observed behavior which could be reliably translated into
attitudes. "Braddock showed a furious intrepidity." "The men
were cheerful [or terrified]." Whether the ascribed attitudes
did correspond to the observations no historian can ever know
unless his sources tell him, but the observed behavior is generally
enough for purposes of literary realism. The military analyst, on
the other hand, may wish to know the genuine psychological
condition of men under a particular strain in battle. He may wish
to assess training preparation, or he may also wish to discover
why a field officer acted in some abnormal way. With the problems of the analyst Parkman was not concerned, for his purposes
were different.

Parkman's re-creation of the Seven Years' War in terms of

its principal campaigns in North America has generally been considered the most masterful and forceful of his writings. Confronted with a solid body of sources for depicting military action, he relied less on panorama or purely scenic effects except where they served a necessary function in the action itself. His description of the surf-thundering coasts of Louisbourg, for example, adds vitally to one's understanding of the precarious amphibious landing of Pepperell and his men in 1745 and Amherst's army in 1758. The "approach march" offered Parkman further occasions to establish the visual immediacy of the day and the event to come, as for instance the British army moving up Lake George in a vast flotilla of little boats on its way to attack Ticonderoga. An actual scene of battle is so largely the sum of many concrete details of movement that the recorded details practically speak for themselves. The historian's choice in organizing them comprises the fundamental problem of recreating the totality of such actions, and it is precisely in Parkman's choice of organization that one can see most clearly the nature of his writing.

To conclude this chapter I shall consider in some detail his organization of two particular incidents in the military campaigns against New France: the battle and defeat of Braddock's army on the Monongahela; and the landing of Wolfe's army and its ascent up the Heights of Abraham.

Parkman's account of Braddock's defeat in 1755 invites some appraisal of his achievement as a literary historian. To be sure, in narrating this incident he was stripped of some of the advantages he brought to his best work. He had never been in battle and had never experienced a military operation, so one is not surprised to find his analysis of maneuver and tactics weak. This particular account, furthermore, did not lend itself to scenic description, nor was he able to build the story around a single individual. Washington comes closest to being the hero, but less from his reported conduct than from Parkman's assertion that he was such. It is also true that Parkman's account of Braddock's defeat is one of the few major incidents in his writings which later historical discoveries show to have been partially inaccurate. The point is worth stressing if only to indicate the high average maintained in the series as a whole; even in this instance his interpretation of the battle was the one which the public of Braddock's day had been led to believe and for which the evidence to contradict it was unavailable until recently. But the British disaster affords one the opportunity to compare the manner in which at least two modern historians have rendered the same incident. Parkman's quality of rendition may at last stand in some perspective. It is unimportant to show him as better or worse than others; a more significant task is to determine his own special gifts. I shall compare his account with those of Lawrence H. Gipson, in *The Great War for the Empire*, and Douglas S. Freeman, in *Young Washington*—two writers for whom, like Parkman, this battle was but an incident in a large historical context, and whose works show them to be historians of major stature, synthesizing the latest researches available to them.[20]

The structure of Parkman's narrative is as follows.[21] Braddock's army, having left behind their heaviest cannon and baggage to follow as it might, approached to within two days' march of Fort Duquesne. They had met with no ambush or attack during their march through the wilderness. By the afternoon of July 9 Braddock, his officers, and his men were confident that they would not be attacked until they had reached the fort, now only a day away. This confidence was due to their having

20. L. H. Gipson, *The Great War for the Empire: the Years of Defeat, 1754–1757*, Vol. 6 of *The British Empire before the American Revolution* (New York, 1946). Hereafter cited as *The Great War*. D. S. Freeman, *Young Washington*, Vol. 2 of *George Washington, a Biography* (New York, C. Scribner's Sons, 1948). Hereafter cited as *Washington*.

21. The following summary, with quotes, is from *M. and W.*, *1*, 220–8, *passim*.

just crossed the Monongahela River unmolested at a spot ideal
for an ambush or an attack upon them. "The men were in-
spirited." As the long column crossed the shallow river Parkman's readers see it as Washington did. There were twelve
hundred men, mostly British regulars, a few Virginia militia and
officers, divided into vanguard and scouts, a working party to
clear a way, some cannon, an advanced guard, the main body,
the wagons, and a rear guard. They were deployed for ambush
but not for a head-on engagement. The forest which they
entered was "dense and heavy . . . choked with bushes." [22]

A war party of eight hundred Indians accompanied by twenty
French soldiers and some Canadians had left the fort earlier,
intending to intercept Braddock at the river, but they were
delayed and met the British head on while on the trail. The
reader first sees the engagement as the British saw it. The vanguard fired two volleys, "cheering lustily," killing the leading
French officer and forcing the Indians to disperse down the
flanks of the column. Parkman then switches to a French point
of view, describing the obvious surprise of the French second-in-
command, who rallied his men with difficulty, holding the trail
while the Indians poured their fire into the long column from
hidden cover on two flanks and a commanding hill. The result
was catastrophic. "The British cheer was heard no more. The
troops broke their ranks and huddled together in a bewildered
mass, shrinking from the bullets that cut them down by scores."

Braddock was unable to restore order from the hopeless confusion and danger. As the vanguard retreated and the main
body advanced, they ran together in confusion. To the chaos
was added the terror of men and officers new to Indian war;
the Virginians might have saved the day with their partisan-

22. Recent scholarship has questioned this last statement. The
scene of engagement was actually fairly "open" woodland with almost no obstructions underfoot. See Stanley Pargellis, "Braddock's
Defeat," *American Historical Review, 41* (1936), 253 ff. Also *Washington*, p. 67.

style deployment had not Braddock forced them to remain in line. They could not have repulsed the savages, but they could have held them until order had been restored.[23] Matters in a moment, however, soon deteriorated beyond any hope of repair. The British fired at their own men; they could see nothing of the enemy. Gallant forays toward the hill were cut down. "The mob of soldiers, stupefied with terror, stood panting, their foreheads beaded with sweat, loading and firing mechanically. . . ." Braddock and Washington tried in vain to rally the army. The officers acted desperately to persuade their men to follow them. Their conduct was "above praise." But one by one they were shot down.[24] At last the army fled down the trail and across the river. Braddock was hit; no one could have stopped the panicked troops. What was left of the army disintegrated. For the final scene the reader is switched to the French fort as Indians return with scalps, plunder, and prisoners whom they burn alive. The French commander is worried whether the English will rally.

Before commenting on this account of the battle I must summarize what Gipson and Freeman did with it. Gipson wrote as a detached scholar, for whom this particular military engagement could occupy at the most a tiny place in an enormously detailed institutional, political, and economic history of the entire British Empire prior to 1763. The problems of political policy and military decision plainly deserved, in his eyes, at least equal attention with action on the battlefield. He chose, consequently, to alternate editorial comment and analysis of general factors with description of action, of which even the latter seldom achieves a direct visual impact. In Gipson's favor

23. Parkman implied that the British should *not* have fought like Indians, that Braddock should have allowed the *Virginians* to do so in order to enable the British to re-form and win with their regular tactics. Simply by relying on reported evidence and his own academic knowledge of Indian tactics Parkman was thus in advance of the traditional "patriotic" view accepted in his day. Cf. Pargellis, p. 253.

24. Pargellis contends that the officers were ultimately more to blame than the men for the failure to gain victory. *Ibid.*, pp. 263 ff.

it must be said that he presented enough strategical and tactical evidence to indicate clearly (which Parkman did not do) who was responsible for the disaster and why it occurred. Few of his facts conflict with Parkman's, and when they do Gipson's must be presumed the more accurate.[25] But Gipson offers no "experience" of the scene. Clichés and occasional rhetorical flourishes attempt to approximate vividness but do not generally succeed, for his imagery is often artificial and seems almost intellectually removed from the reader. Gipson told what the British Empire was doing at Monongahela, but something is lost in the telling.

Freeman's account bears readier comparison with Parkman's. Though he possessed newer and better data than Parkman, his interpretation, as well as his use of fact, was similar.[26] His description built minute details into a pattern which Parkman avoided in the interest of rapid, forceful movement. Freeman solved the problem of immediacy in a very different way. His work is a meticulously faithful study of Washington's mind and life in action, and Braddock's campaign proved to be one of the major events in Washington's early career. Freeman's account of the river crossing is far more complex than Parkman's, for he views it as Washington had viewed it, with the reactions of a critical, observant colonel. The opening fire sent "George . . . stiff in the saddle at the first crash. . . . Braddock listened intently. . . . Let one of the younger aides go forward and find out what was happening."

But Freeman did not cripple his narrative by riding a formula to death. His reader glimpses a wide sweep of the battle, even though the information supplied him is limited entirely to the information available to the British officers. This technique serves a special purpose. Freeman's battle scene is built as a

25. For Gipson's style see especially *The Great War*, pp. 94–6, including an excellent analysis of Braddock's failure to secure the hill. Gipson has often presented a better account than Parkman on certain subjects. See his Vol. 5, chapter "Les Habitants."
26. *Washington*, chap. 5, *passim*.

problem in command, intrinsically interesting in itself, but also as a direct re-creation of the problems which had faced Braddock (and therefore Washington) and of the way he reacted. Freeman renders vividly the confusion of warfare, the drama and heroic character of the event, providing a realistic environment for the purposes of subjective military analysis. He does not choose to cross the line of battle until it is over and the scene has been completely enacted; only then does a long discussion of the campaign take place, a critique generally more satisfactory and complete than Gipson's. As this information is "experiential" and immediate, so is the writing; the impact, like Parkman's, is direct. But Freeman's reader, unlike Parkman's, becomes virtually one of the officers. He is caught up in a subjective swirl of impressions, flashes, and emotions that attempt to duplicate the immediacy of being a participant in the decisions and events of the moment. The style is worthy of Parkman, and the result is a faithful "experience of seeing." But the ultimate framework is biography, and Freeman did not attempt to define the event except in terms of one man who was there. Though the sights are microscopic, within this drop of water there is no universe.

Parkman's achievement was to reconcile Gipson's scope with Freeman's visual directness. His detached camera eye peering over the shoulder of a dozen combatants records a variety of sights from all parts of the battle, and it never attempts an internal or subjective view. Many of his descriptions are confusing, in particular a paragraph discussing the role of the Virginians and their tree fighting, wherein Parkman seems to contradict himself three times in three sentences.[27] In general he made no attempt to offer a "military" picture, and this is well; he could not have done so as an expert, nor were his purposes served by so doing. He struck for the quality of the scene itself, the interplay of rival forces, the dramatic possibilities for depicting masses of men in heroic or desperate attitudes, yet

27. *M. and W., 1,* 225.

depicted with no flourishes of heroic writing. His readers are
made aware of large historical forces as they clash in a single
concentrated scene. Many themes from the earlier histories one
finds recapitulated here: the Indian savagery, the wilderness
which confronted and changed the men who wandered into
it from their "higher" worlds, the terror of the unknown made
a literal and fatal fact ("We would fight if we could see anybody
to fight with," wrote one officer), and the impulses of courage
and gallantry, however useless, in the face of chaos. One not
only senses the larger scene within the specific event; he "under-
stands" the event in terms of the basic themes in Parkman's
history.

Success in scaling the Heights of Abraham with a force of
four thousand men in the early morning of September 10, 1759
depended upon an intricate mass of preliminaries. Parkman
conveys this event with a competence and artistry which he
matched nowhere else. Hanging the thread of action on the
chesslike interplay of two forces, he offers his reader Wolfe's
evolving strategy simultaneously with the plans and circumstances of the besieged French under Montcalm. We look over
the shoulders of both men, as it were, and grasp not only a personal element of decision and doubt but a more distant view of
the very process of interaction. We learn of Wolfe's anxiety over
the late season and his decision to abandon the campaign should
his last gamble fail; we then are told of the desperate situation
in Quebec, where famine and discontent raced against the hope
of an English departure. Wolfe's strategy finally crystallized:
a constant series of feints along the river so confused the French
that, when the path was discovered and the landing made,
Bougainville's mobile shore defense was miles away, exhausted
from chasing up and down the shore. The reader knows all this
and more: the French sentries had confused the British boats
with the regular French patrols who passed by every night
(Wolfe counted on this confusion); Vergor had failed to post

his men; Guienne's battalion was absent from its post; and Bougainville's message of alarm was never to reach the sentries. Consequently with the actual landing the reader has observed an interplay of critical forces and the momentous chances that underlay it. Parkman created not only the complete actuality of fact but the intrinsic drama of the moment. It savors of the heroic design, and time after time Parkman's chief interest in history seems to have been to extract from its authentic record a quality of permanent human endeavor. He strove to find in the actions of a multitude of men certain timeless characteristics that did not depend on local circumstance but, when re-expressed as part of history, can be made real only in the context of local circumstance. The courageous decision of Wolfe, gambling against a fabulous train of odds, creates tension in the reader merely through his knowing of it. The drama re-exists in his own consciousness, and he becomes absorbed into the moment of time and the few yards of space. "As they neared their destination, the tide bore them in towards the shore, and the mighty wall of rock and forest towered in darkness on their left. The dead stillness was suddenly broken by the sharp *Qui vive!* of a French sentry, invisible in the thick gloom." [28]

The improvised answer, the boats moving on, the second challenge and reply, the boats sweeping into the cove could not have been told with more compression and swiftness. Finally the forward party ascended the path, surprised and repulsed the guard. Then occurs a passage which conveys the intolerable suspense of the party still on the beach. The point of view is Wolfe's:

> The main body of troops waited in their boats by the edge of the strand. The heights nearby were cleft by a great ravine choked with forest trees; and in its depths ran a little brook . . . which, swollen by the late rains, fell plashing in the stillness over a rock. Other than this no sound could reach

28. *Ibid.*, 3, 129.

the strained ear of Wolfe but the gurgle of the tide and the
cautious climbing of his advanced parties. . . . At length
from the top came the sound of musket-shots, followed by
loud huzzas, and he knew that his men were masters of the
position. The word was given; the troops leaped from their
boats and scaled the heights, some here, some there, clutch-
ing at trees and bushes, their muskets slung at their backs.
. . . In the gray light of the morning the long file of red-
coated soldiers moved quickly upward and formed in order
on the plateau above.[29]

Although knowing of the advanced party's success, the reader
shares in Wolfe's suspense. The device is a simple one. Wolfe
strained his ears for a clue, and what he heard was the splash
of water and the river sucking at the beach. The sudden release
of tension at the sound of success fortifies one's own sense of the
silence and its tiny sounds that preceded. Details of this sort
renew one's identity with the experience of Wolfe; they were
as much Parkman's as the record's, and hence the "actuality"
in rendering them. But Parkman did not create the scene. It
existed in historical fact, and its details, being of a common
human experience, are potentially real for every reader. By
presenting the facts as he did Parkman helped to objectify for
his readers what their own experience would tell them could
be real.

In like manner Parkman wrote the history of New France
from its beginnings to its downfall, a continuity of events determined by a complex interaction of men and time and place.
Because he developed his style as an idiom of visual and personal experience common to himself, the reader, and the men
who had participated, Parkman not only re-created the actuality
of history but suggested in some measure its very meaning.

29. *Ibid.*, 3, 131.

CHAPTER FOUR

Parkman's Achievement

Romance, being in its origin a local sentiment,
gave a new significance to place, to the scene of
action. . . . To the new school, "Where did it
happen?" would be quite as important as "How
did it happen?" Indeed, the two are hardly to be
separated.

           —G. M. YOUNG, *Last Essays*

F EW historians, indeed few writers of any sort, have withstood the changing literary fashions of three generations so well as has Francis Parkman. An age which no longer reads Hildreth or Bancroft or Motley, which finds most of Prescott tedious and neglects Carlyle and Macaulay, finds Parkman's history of New France and his account of the Oregon trail fresh in impact and contemporary in style. The vigor and imaginativeness of his prose in fact seem to assure him among current readers as enduring, if not as widespread, a popularity as that assured to Hawthorne and Emerson and even Sir Walter Scott. Even in the art of imaginative writing Parkman the historian excelled many of the professional novelists of his age. The reasons for this are not obvious, but possibly they provide a clue to Parkman's talent for writing history. I wish to conclude my study with some reflections on the quality of Parkman's writing as it compares with the quality found in the works of a few of his outstanding contemporaries in England and America. In so doing I bear in mind the following questions: Even granting his success, was his style unique after all? What has caused his writings to endure? May present-day historians profit from his achievement?

Parkman's biographers have established with some certainty the pattern of his reading and the books most appealing to him in his early years.[1] He read widely and intently throughout his life; though his debt to the style of others was small, it was not due to his ignorance of the literature of both French and English history. Acquaintance with Parkman's writings as well as with many of his favorite writers leads me to conclude that he studiously avoided the style and the mannerisms of historians while absorbing their facts and their ideas. On the other hand his style was markedly influenced by the idiom and the verbal techniques of Scott and Cooper and the romantic poets. He developed style consciously and deliberately to serve his own ends, and one need only glance at the writings of the historians who could have been his models to see how much his differed from theirs.

Parkman's style, for example, had little in common with Carlyle's. The biographer of Frederick the Great gave full play to his imaginative use of original phrase, coloring the intimate anecdotes of the Prussian court with a breezy idiom so personal as to have invited few imitators. In scenes of battle, where comparison is readier, Carlyle failed to provide the sense of careful, scrupulous accuracy which one learns to trust in Parkman. There is no doubt that the latter had read Carlyle, but there is equal certainty that he borrowed neither Carlyle's subjective and passionate thesis of the Great Man nor the fluid, erratic structure of symbol and image which conveyed it. Nor did Parkman's enduring qualities derive from Macaulay, whose history of England, nevertheless, one can at least argue possesses a technique

1. See particularly Charles H. Farnham, *A Life of Francis Parkman* (Boston, 1900), pp. 72–83; and Mason Wade, *Francis Parkman, Heroic Historian,* pp. 11, 341, *passim.*

as suitable to its subject as was Parkman's to his. Macaulay's
eloquent literary style embellished an imposing design of political events with frequent personal episode, colorful analogy,
and generalized statement. He was best in the brief essay, in-
terpreting a historical movement or a social phenomenon with
a degree of imagination and sophistication Parkman seldom attempted. But Macaulay cannot so often convince the modern
reader, as can Parkman, of the time and place and setting. Parkman wrote no tract and urged no special view. His narrative was
built on the particular and authentic detail of a moment, and
hence he tended to avoid the easy generalization which destroys
for readers the quality of immediacy of action and movement.

Parkman's literary achievement appears more sharply defined
if he is viewed in company with Irving and Prescott, two writers
whom he had read with great interest, and whose historical
themes and conceptions were closer to his own. When Irving
turned his varied talents to history, one of his most successful
ventures was to write up the records and journals of the early
overland explorations to the West Coast; here he demonstrated
great facility and casualness of style, and his account of the
country through which his mountain men traveled has been
found surprisingly authentic. The vividness of *Astoria* and its
accuracy of detail, however, Irving derived not from his personal experiences but from a careful devotion to fur company
records and a wide reading in current literature about the West
and its occupants. His prose does not sparkle, and despite the
gripping train of incidents which throng his account, the narrative lacks the authority of that direct verification of scene
which Parkman brought to comparable episodes of the wilderness frontier. Urbane and at times even perfunctory, Irving's
treatment of major historical themes ranks him much below
Parkman in scholarship and particularly in the enduring aspects
of style.

Prescott's principal works antedated Parkman's only thirty
years. By almost any standard of historiography his *Conquest*

of Mexico stands as a monumental achievement. But Prescott
clothed his narrative in one of the most forbidding and man-
nered stylistic idioms since the age of Samuel Johnson. Through
his pages there marches an endless procession of complex clas-
sical sentences, ponderous with formal allusions and Latinized
rhetoric as tailored as a changing of the guard. Prescott's modern
reader is apt to feel screened off from the action and movement
of the story, which grows more opaque as its conventions of
style tend to date both its substance and its texture. Vivid and
powerful as are many of his descriptions—few historians have
ever sustained such breathless suspense of action through so
lengthy a chronicle—Prescott nevertheless lacked either Parkman's gift or his opportunity for fashioning the materials of history in direct, personal terms experienced and translated as
immediate fact. Both men found in the same elements of a grand
pageant of heroism and conflict the opportunity for a lifetime
of literary devotion, but while the younger man evolved for
himself a historical idiom in advance of his day, the older man
turned to the models of a tradition dying even as he wrote.
Parkman's sentences were often as short and unambiguous as
the language of military command. He was far more careful
than Prescott to limit his account to verifiable events and authentic records, and in matters of color and drama he took
further care to render episodes which his personal experience
could in some measure fortify. Prescott's scenes of Indian barbarism may in fact be as valid as Parkman's, but they seem over-
done and artificial; the color strikes one as Prescott's, not Aztec,
and the continuous clash of great forces appears less convincing
in his labored style than in the stark simplicity of Parkman's un-
qualified sentences. And finally the refusal of Parkman to structure his narrative and expository record in order to support
some prearranged conclusion marked a distinct advance over
Prescott's concept of literary history. To be sure the perfunctory
morals which Prescott drew from the thread of his narrative
were generally hedged about with qualifications and scarcely

offend even modern readers; his history nevertheless reflects a conception of imposing moral design common to Macaulay, Bancroft, and even Carlyle but which Parkman avoided for the sake of allowing his narrative to speak for itself. Striking for balance and dispassionate objectivity Parkman stripped personal idiom and eccentricity from his prose and a priori design from his narrative structure to a degree scarcely conceivable before his day. It was, I think, a notable achievement for a 19th-century writer.

I have suggested that in matters of structure and style Parkman owed more to purely imaginative writers than to historians. His finest images at times recall the fervid graphic phrases of Byron's *Childe Harold* (which he read throughout his life), and some scholars have detected in his handling of scenes and movements of men the influence of Scott and Cooper.[2] Ultimately Parkman's own artistry surpassed the idiom of these men, who really belonged to an earlier tradition; but in terms of his attitude toward the past, a critical factor in the evaluation of any historian, Parkman stands in an important relationship to Scott and Cooper, a relationship that helps to explain the effectiveness and the achievement of his writing.

Scott and Cooper as historical novelists were engrossed in the romance of place and time; it is significant that they held the facts of history in large respect. Building incidents on particular, authentic settings, which they had observed sufficiently to be able to describe for themselves, they ransacked the records of past events in order to establish as real an environment as the limits of their craft permitted. Their settings usually fall in a frontier area among people suitably removed from the tame and advanced social settings of the reader so as to add color and zest to already unfamiliar exploits. Though the characters and their emotional entanglements were fictitious and often painfully unreal, the flavor of the settings in Scott and Cooper remain

2. See, for example, Bliss Perry, "Some Personal Qualities of Francis Parkman," *Yale Review, 13* (1924), 443 ff.

as convincing today as they did a century ago when Parkman read them. Scott and Cooper wrote often of the 17th- and 18th-century borderlands, of battles and deeds of valor, of old chieftains and young heroes, of renegades and of loyal followers. Theirs were regions of crags and glens, of forests and lakes and manor houses. Their stories frequently centered on combat and military campaigns. But above all they integrated the men they created with a specific action in time and place, and to the action they added a clear, uncomplicated style and a considerable degree of both personal and historical verification. These writers anticipated, and indeed shaped, the tradition of the romantic novel based on the application of a literary imagination to history.

Writing of Cooper's most popular tale, *The Last of the Mohicans,* Parkman noted that its author, for historical background, had borrowed freely from the published recollections of a Mrs. Grant. But "Mrs. Grant's facts—for as such we are to take them —have an air of fiction; while Cooper's fiction wears the aspect of solid fact." Though the scene of Hawkeye's fight with the "Mingoes" never actually occurred, Parkman paid tribute to its reality, and declared of Cooper's book in general: "It takes needless liberties with history; and though it would be folly to demand that an historical novelist should always conform to received authorities, yet it is certainly desirable that he should not unnecessarily set them at defiance; since the incidents of the novel are apt to remain longer in the memory than those of the less palatable history." [3] Cooper's novels, he concluded, concerned themselves not with "fine ideas" but with life.

With very little difficulty one can deduce from these observations Parkman's own ideal for the historian. History can lend both color and verisimilitude to the novelist's tale. Likewise, within their limits, the novelist's imagination and observation can transform the recorded event into readable history. It is

3. "The Works of James Fenimore Cooper," *The North American Review, 74* (January 1852), 151–2.

said that Parkman's first ambition was to write poetry and heroic novels. He came to prefer history. Better than creating what one hopes was valid experience is to re-create what is known to have been valid experience. Art is just as necessary for the second as for the first, because both depend on the coordinating activity of the writer to transmit what he uses to the reader in terms of experience common to both. Parkman had experienced at least in a minimum sense the wilderness, the culture of the Indian, the monastery, and the heroic adventure. In other realms, such as military action, his imagination and interest had made him peculiarly capable of writing with vivid realism. Simple, forceful prose comes naturally enough to the treatment of action, whether in novels or in history; Parkman's gifts included the ability to impart to the exposition and analysis of grand historical movements and social forces the vividness and flexibility of imaginative writing.

If any single conclusion emerges from a study of Parkman's writings it is that he wrote only one of an almost infinite number of histories which could have been written from the same documentary material. Modern historians know how precarious were the assumptions of some of their fathers, the "scientific" historians; not only did completeness seem possible to the extremists of that school but the very act of recording history seemed to them to assure total objectivity, a freedom from the subjective pitfalls of selecting one's material, and, above all, a logical sequence of writing, scientifically guided, as it were, by the necessities of the subject matter. If the fallacies of such assumptions are clearer or better known now than they once were, it should also be clear how fortunate it was that Parkman wrote in a tradition mostly self-determined and untouched by them. To be sure, he may have written under the conviction that objectivity is attainable and that the careful historian will be able to set down the *total* truth of events. The fact remains that such a conviction did not make him avoid or shun the his-

tory which he did write in order to pursue an unattainable ideal
of "scientific" completeness. His was one version of the long and
complex record of New France. No one would wish to re-write
his version today, and few would suggest that his precludes all
others. The important thing is that his version remains valid.

The qualities of his achievement are evident. He was a
pioneer historian who perceived in his theme the forces and
actions which constitute great history. The clash of cultures,
the struggle of men with their environment, their zest for life,
their ambitions and their follies were for Parkman the basic
essentials of the human story. Records showed them to him as
true. He in turn presented his theme in language stripped bare
of every device that might detract from the pure content. This
was a truly significant achievement. But there is more to it than
that.

I have attempted to show some of the preconceptions and
interests which led Parkman to discover and to develop his
version of the record, and I have analyzed the basic components
of that version. I have attempted to point out a functional relation between his style and his own approach to the documented
fact, suggesting that by his artistry with words he achieved a
visual fidelity to the truth which he himself saw in the record
and verified in his own experiences. His history is mainly a
human drama of action and exploit in which qualities of character often shine through the factual record of what occurred.
There is much more besides, enough more to constitute a valid
structure of history without destroying the intrinsic values of
the individual incidents. At one end of the structure is a
thematic pattern grounded in recorded fact. At the other are
its component human experiences, which are grounded in the
reader by a process of artistic re-creation. The two experiences
correspond, and the result is a synthesis of the fact and its
presentation as history. Parkman chose only one version of the
truth; his genius made it certain that we would apprehend its
reality. In this lies his enduring achievement.

Pet Friends Forever

Problem Pup

by Diana G. Gallagher

illustrated by Adriana Isabel Juárez Puglisi

capstone

is published by
Picture Window Books,
A Capstone Imprint
1710 Roe Crest Drive
North Mankato, Minnesota 56003
www.capstonepub.com

Library of Congress Cataloging-in-Publication Data
Gallagher, Diana G., author.
Problem pup / by Diana G. Gallagher; illustrated by Adriana Puglisi.
pages cm. -- (Pet friends forever)

Summary: Kyle's friend Drew has adopted a dog from the shelter, but the
boys need to teach it manners and obedience or Drew's parents are going
to send it back.

ISBN 978-1-4795-2176-0 (hardcover) -- ISBN 978-1-4795-3802-7 (pbk.)
-- ISBN 978-1-4795-5232-0 (ebook)

1. Dogs--Behavior--Juvenile fiction. 2. Dogs--Training--Juvenile
fiction. 3. Dogs--Juvenile fiction. [1. Dogs--Training--Fiction. 2.
Dogs--Fiction. 3. Pet adoption--Fiction.] I. Puglisi, Adriana,
illustrator. II. Title.
PZ7.G13543Pr 2014
813.6--dc23
2013028614

Designer: Kristi Carlson
Image Credits: Shutterstock/Kudryashka (pattern)

Printed in China.
092013   007749WAIMANS14

TABLE OF CONTENTS

Clinic Chaos

"C'mon, Rex!" Kyle called as he ran down the street toward his mom's veterinary clinic Friday afternoon.

Rex, Kyle's yellow Labrador retriever, ran beside him, leaping and turning in circles. Rex could sense that Kyle was excited, so he was excited, too.

Kyle yanked open the front door of Dr. Blake's Veterinary Clinic and hurried inside. Practically bursting with excitement, he pulled a paper out of his pocket. He couldn't wait to show his mom how well he'd done on his math test.

Behind the counter, Lillian, the clinic's receptionist, smiled at him. "You look like you're in a good mood," she said.

"I am," Kyle said. "I got a hundred percent on my math test!"

"Congrat—" Lillian started to say. But just then, Rex came charging past Kyle into the waiting room.

"Look out!" Lillian shouted.

Rex's leash got tangled around Kyle's feet, making him lose his balance. Kyle fell against the magazine rack, knocking it to the ground with a loud *CRASH!* Papers scattered across the floor. Rex yelped with surprise and jumped away, knocking into a cat carrier on the floor. The cat inside hissed angrily.

Across the room, a small poodle was waiting with its owner. The dog pulled against his leash and yapped at the cat. His front feet came off the floor when he barked, and he squeaked when he landed.

Angry hisses continued to come from inside the cat carrier. Finally, the cat's owner picked up the carrier and put it on his lap. He shot an irritated glance at Kyle and Rex.

The little poodle continued yapping and tugging at his leash to get free.

"Bailey, no!" the poodle's owner said, pulling the little dog away.

Everything seemed to be calming down a bit . . . then Rex started barking. The poodle immediately looked at Rex and jumped out of its owner's lap. Rex dropped into a play bow on his front end.

"Bailey! Get away from that animal right now!" the woman holding the poodle's leash hollered.

"Sorry!" Kyle said, grabbing Rex by the collar. "He won't hurt him. He just wants to play."

The poodle suddenly seemed to realize that Rex was bigger. The little dog turned tail and scrambled to safety between his owner's feet.

Rex thought the poodle was playing. He jumped toward the little dog.

"Get away!" Bailey's owner hollered again.

Lillian came out from behind the front desk to stand between the two dogs. "It's okay, Mrs. Stone. Rex won't hurt Bailey," she said. She glared at Kyle. "But he's being a very bad dog today!"

Kyle tried to pull Rex back. "Stop it, Rex!" he said firmly. "Come here."

But Rex wanted to play with his new poodle pal. He didn't budge.

Just then, Kyle's mom came walking into the waiting room. "What is going on out here?" she demanded.

"That dog attacked Bailey," the poodle's owner said, pointing at Rex.

"No, he didn't!" Kyle protested. "He just wanted to play!"

"Outside, Kyle," Dr. Blake said. She pointed to the front door and gave her son an irritated look. "Now!"

Bailey started yapping all over again, and Kyle had to drag Rex out the front door. His mom followed, closing the door behind her. The noise in the waiting room immediately quieted.

"Now what happened?" Dr. Blake asked.

"It wasn't Rex's fault, Mom," Kyle said. "I knocked over the magazine rack. And the cat started hissing, and the poodle started barking, and Rex wouldn't shut up. But he wasn't trying to hurt that dog. He just wanted to play."

Dr. Blake sighed and rubbed her forehead. "Kyle, we've talked about this. What are the Rex rules?" she asked.

Kyle's shoulders sagged and he looked at the ground. "That Rex has to behave when he's in the clinic," he mumbled.

"*All* the time," his mom said. "No exceptions. That means no barking and no playing with the patients. I can't have him upsetting people."

Kyle nodded. "I know," he said. "Sorry, Mom."

"I think it might be a good idea if Rex stays away from the clinic for a while," Dr. Blake said. "If there's another incident like this, he won't be allowed in the clinic at all."

Dr. Blake went back inside the clinic, and Kyle turned to walk next door to their house. Rex trailed along next to him quietly. He seemed to sense he was in trouble.

As they walked into the kitchen, Kyle remembered his perfect math test. He was still holding the paper, but it didn't seem that exciting anymore. Rex was in big trouble with Mom. And that meant Kyle was, too.

Bad Dog Fix-It Plan

A few minutes later, the doorbell rang. Kyle opened the door and saw Mia, his best friend and next-door neighbor, on the porch.

"Hey, Mia," Kyle said. "What's up?"

"I was hoping you and Rex would want to go to the park with me," Mia said.

"Sure," Kyle replied. "Come on in while I grab my shoes and coat."

The two kids made their way to the kitchen, where Rex was lying on the floor. He looked over at Mia and Kyle when they walked in, but he didn't move.

"What's wrong with Rex?" Mia asked. "He looks depressed."

"I think he knows he's in trouble," Kyle explained. "He went a little nuts at the clinic."

"What did he do?" Mia asked.

Kyle sat down to pull on his shoes and told Mia what happened. "If Rex messes up again, he'll be banned from the clinic for good," he finished. "My mom was really mad."

"Maybe Rex just wasn't in the mood to listen," Mia suggested.

Kyle sighed. Rex wasn't in the mood to listen a lot of the time. Especially if he was busy chasing squirrels. Or eating. Or smelling something. Or napping. "You need to remind him that you're the boss," Mia said.

Kyle nodded. "You're right," he said. "He already knows all the obedience commands."

"But he only does them when he feels like it," Mia pointed out. "He has to do them when you say so."

"All the time," Kyle agreed. "Even if a squirrel kicks him in the nose!"

Mia giggled. "Or it rains dog treats."

"Or he smells pizza," Kyle said. "When I say *come*, I mean it!"

Rex's ear twitched when he heard the command, but he didn't sit up to obey.

Mia sighed. "You've got a lot of work to do," she said.

"No kidding," Kyle said. "So let's get started."

Kyle grabbed Rex's leash, and the three of them headed to the dog park. He usually let Rex relax and check out all the doggy-delicious smells along the way, but today, he made the yellow Lab heel and stay by his side.

Rex wasn't happy about it. He kept trying to veer off the sidewalk to sniff the trees. Every time Rex pulled on his leash, Kyle made him stop and sit for a minute. After the fourth stop, Rex finally gave in and walked nicely.

The dog park was extra crowded by the time they made it there. There were dogs catching Frisbees, digging in the sand, and rolling on the grass. Two black Labs dashed through tunnels and leapt over jumps on the agility course. A few tired dogs napped under benches while their owners read or talked on cell phones.

"Wow!" Mia exclaimed when they entered the fenced playground for dogs. "There must be fifty dogs here today!"

"Maybe more," Kyle said as he looked around. "I've never seen it this crowded before."

"Are you sure this is the best place to practice?" Mia asked.

"It's perfect!" Kyle said. He stopped, and Rex sat down next to him.

"But there's so much going on here," Mia said.

"That's why it's perfect," Kyle said. "I have to teach Rex to ignore the other stuff and just listen to me."

Just then, a man with a German shepherd ran by. Rex whined, wiggled, and started to stand up. He wanted to run, too.

"Sit!" Kyle ordered.

Rex whined again, but he stayed sitting.

"Good boy," Kyle said. He pulled a treat out of his pocket and fed it to Rex. "Okay, let's get started."

Kyle tugged lightly on Rex's leash to get the dog's attention. Then he dropped the leash and held his hand in front of Rex's face. "Stay!"

Kyle walked a few feet away, then stopped and turned around to face Rex. The dog was still sitting where Kyle had left him. But when he saw Kyle looking at him, Rex stood up again.

"Stay!" Kyle called. He held his hand out toward the yellow Lab. Rex quickly stopped moving and stood where he was while Kyle walked over.

"Sit," Kyle said as he picked up the leash again. Rex sat, and Mia applauded.

"That was great!" a boy's voice said.

Kyle glanced over and saw Drew Martin sitting on a nearby bench. A white spaniel with big black spots sat on the ground near his feet. Drew went to their school, but he was in a different fourth-grade class, so Kyle didn't know him very well.

Mia walked over to pet Drew's dog. "What's his name?" she asked.

"Lucky," Drew said. He nodded toward Rex. "Can he do any other tricks?"

"Sure," Kyle replied. He had Rex lie down, stay, and shake. Rex must have been in the mood to listen. He didn't make any mistakes.

Feeling more confident, Kyle tossed a stick a few feet away. "Leave it!" he told Rex before the dog could run after it.

Rex stared at the stick. He whined softly, but he didn't move to get it.

"Good boy!" Kyle said proudly. He knew how hard it was for Rex to resist running after the stick. He was lucky to have such a well-behaved dog.

Suddenly, Drew's dog sprang to his feet, rushed forward, and grabbed the stick. Rex immediately barked and chased after Lucky. That was Rex's stick!

"Lucky!" Drew shouted. "Put that down!"

But Lucky didn't listen. He took off running, holding the stick proudly in his mouth. Rex chased him, and the two dogs ran in circles around the park. Every time the boys and Mia tried to catch them, they raced away again.

"Rex!" Kyle called to his dog. "Come back here! Now!"

But Rex seemed to be done listening for the day. He ignored Kyle and kept chasing after Lucky.

Mia sighed. "Rex was doing so well!" she said, shaking her head.

"It's my fault," Drew said. "I was so busy watching you that I forgot to hold onto Lucky's leash. You're a good dog trainer, Kyle."

"Not good enough," Kyle said. "If Rex doesn't start listening to me, my mom will never let him back in her clinic."

"I wish that's all I had to worry about," Drew mumbled.

"What do you mean?" Mia asked.

"I've been begging for a dog for years," Drew explained. "My parents finally decided I was old enough to take care of one, so they let me adopt Lucky from the shelter a few months ago."

"That's good, isn't it?" Kyle asked.

"Yeah, except we didn't count on getting a dog that digs in the trash, chews up shoes, and doesn't come when he's called," Drew explained. He looked upset. "I've been trying to train him since we brought him home, but it's not working."

"Well, it takes time to train a dog," Kyle pointed out.

"I know," Drew said, "but if Lucky doesn't learn to behave, I'm worried that my parents are going to make me get rid of him."

"What?" Mia gasped.

Drew nodded unhappily. "That's what my dad said yesterday," he told them. "He was really upset. He said that if Lucky doesn't start to show some improvement by next Saturday, he's gone."

Not if we can help it, Kyle thought. "Why don't you and Lucky meet Rex and me here on Saturday," he suggested. "I have to work on his training anyway. We can work on Lucky's at the same time."

"That would be great!" Drew said, sounding grateful. "I need all the help I can get!"

The Misty Mystery

Rex walked quietly on the way home, but Kyle knew it was mostly because he was tired after his game of keep-away with Lucky.

"I can't believe Drew's parents would make him get rid of Lucky," Mia said.

Kyle nodded. His mom might be annoyed with Rex, but she'd never get rid of him. "Maybe Drew's parents just don't understand dogs," he suggested.

"At least Drew wants to learn," Mia said. "Hopefully you can help him since you're training Rex anyway."

"I hope so," Kyle said. "Lucky's bad habits can be fixed. It'll just take time."

"I wish Misty's bad habits could be fixed," Mia said with a sigh. "She's been worse than ever lately."

"Worse?" Kyle said. That was hard to believe. Mia's cat, Misty, never listened. She was so mean she could chase dogs out of the yard and take down skateboarders. Once she'd even dropped a live beetle in Mia's cereal bowl.

"It's too bad cats can't be trained like dogs," Mia added.

Some can, but not Misty, Kyle thought. Misty did what she wanted when she wanted, and nobody argued.

"What's she doing now?" Kyle asked.

"Last night at dinner she crouched under my chair and clawed at my feet," Mia said. "She wouldn't stop, so we had to lock her outside until we finished."

Misty clawed Kyle's feet all the time. But going after Mia was new.

"And yesterday afternoon she shredded the mail," Mia said. "All my mom's catalogs have holes in them. She was *not* happy."

"Has Misty ever done that before?" Kyle asked.

Mia shook her head. "No. I don't know why she's doing it now."

"Maybe she's just bored and trying to get more attention," Kyle suggested.

"Maybe," Mia said. "Let's go to Mr. J's and get her a new catnip mouse. She loves those."

Mr. J's Pet Haven had been in business for thirty years. Kyle and Mia didn't shop anywhere else for dog and cat supplies. Some things were cheaper at the big chain pet store, but Mr. J knew all his customers by name. And no one knew more about pets.

A bell chimed as Kyle and Mia pushed open the door to Mr. J's Pet Haven. "Don't want any!" Jethro, Mr. J's parrot, squawked as soon as they walked inside.

"Hi, Jethro!" Mia said. "What's up?"

The bird let out a whistle and bobbed his head. "I'm hungry!" he said.

Mia picked up a cracker from the bowl on the counter and held it out to the bird. "Here you go," she said.

Jethro took the cracker with his beak and swallowed it in one bite. As soon as it was gone, he squawked, "Get lost!"

Kyle smiled. The parrot used to live at Mr. J's house. He'd learned to talk by listening to Mr. J's kids.

"That bird is such a brat sometimes!" Mr. J said with a laugh. "What brings you two in today? Anything I can help with?"

"I need a new catnip toy for Misty," Mia said. "And some treats. She's been acting a little weird lately."

"Weird how?" Mr. J asked.

"Clawing at my feet and ripping up the mail," Mia said.

"Some animals get cranky when they get older," Mr. J suggested. "Could that be it?"

Mia shook her head. "Misty isn't old," she said. "She's only four."

"Besides, she was born cranky," Kyle added. "We think she might just be bored."

"That could be it," Mr. J said. "It's hard to tell sometimes since our pets can't tell us what's bothering them. We have to figure it out."

Kyle and Mia followed Mr. J to the back of the store where the cat supplies were kept. He quickly gathered up Misty's new toy and treats.

"Why do some dogs chew stuff and play with trash?" Kyle asked.

"All puppies chew," Mr. J said. "Owners have to teach them that dog toys are okay and everything else is not. And training takes time. Some people don't want to be bothered."

Maybe that's why Lucky's first owner took him to the shelter, Kyle thought.

"And dogs can get into the trash for a lot of reasons," Mr. J continued as they walked back to the front of the store. "Sometimes dogs get nervous when they're left alone. Trash keeps them busy and calms them down."

"Rex used to get into our trash," Kyle said. "But I don't think it calmed him down."

Mr. J laughed. "Sometimes dogs do it just because ripping up smelly stuff is fun," he said.

Lucky is definitely the smelly fun type, Kyle decided.

Mr. J rang up Mia's purchases. "I hope these help with Misty," he said.

"Me, too," Mia said. "I have to wear three pairs of socks to protect my toes when I'm sleeping!"

Whatever Works

When Kyle and Rex arrived at the dog park on Saturday morning, Drew and Lucky were already waiting. Rex and Lucky sniffed noses to say hello, then Kyle made Rex sit. Lucky pranced and pulled on his leash. He wanted to play.

"Did you bring any treats with you?" Kyle asked.

"Yep, a whole bag," Drew said, pulling a bag out of his pocket. "But I don't know if they'll help at all. Training Lucky might be hopeless. Every time he went near the trash last night, I told him, 'No!' but he still dragged garbage all over the kitchen."

"Well, we can't teach him to be a perfect dog in a week," Kyle said. "But we can teach him how to behave a little better."

"I don't know," Drew said. He still didn't look convinced.

"Training a dog isn't easy," Kyle said. "You'll have to be tough, and it'll take a lot of time. So we'll have to cheat a little."

"What do you mean?" Drew asked.

"Your parents won't care why Lucky stops chewing stuff and playing with trash as long as he stops, right?" Kyle said.

Drew nodded. "Right. They just want me to take some responsibility for him. But how do I get him to leave the trash alone?"

"Simple," Kyle said. "Just make sure you take the trash out every night and put an empty bag in the kitchen can. Lucky can't scatter trash if there isn't any."

"That's genius!" Drew exclaimed.

"I don't know about that," Kyle said with a laugh. "I just know from experience. That's what I had to do with Rex."

"What about chewing?" Drew asked. "I read online that using hot sauce works."

"It works on table legs," Kyle said. "I had to use it on ours when Rex was a puppy. But if Lucky is chewing on shoes, it might not be a good idea. Your parents probably don't want to put their feet in hot-sauce shoes."

"Ugh, no!" Drew made a face.

"Lucky needs some chew toys," Kyle said.

"We got him some," Drew said. "But he likes shoes and books better."

"Then you can't leave anything lying around," Kyle said. "If Lucky can't reach it, he can't chew it."

Drew scratched Lucky behind the ears. "What about coming when he's called?" he asked. "I can't do that for him."

"No, we have to trick him," Kyle said. He took a ball and a treat out of his backpack. Then he took Rex off his leash and threw the ball. "Go get it, Rex!"

Rex immediately raced to fetch the ball. Drew had a hard time holding Lucky back. He wanted to go after Rex.

"Here, boy!" Kyle yelled as Rex ran back.

The yellow Lab ran back to Kyle, sat down, and dropped the ball at his feet. Kyle checked to make sure Lucky was watching. Then he gave Rex a treat.

Lucky whined.

"You'll get one, too, Lucky," Kyle said. "You just have to earn it. Ready to try, Drew?"

"I guess," Drew said. "But Lucky won't bring the ball back. He'll just run around with it."

"Not if Rex has the ball," Kyle explained. "Lucky will follow him. Just keep calling for him to come to you. And give him a treat when he gets to you."

"Okay," Drew said. He unclipped Lucky's leash, and Kyle threw the ball. Both dogs took off after it. Lucky got to the ball first. He picked it up and started running in a big circle around the park.

"Now what?" Drew asked, sounding frustrated.

"Keep yelling 'come!' and hold out the treat," Kyle said.

"Come, Lucky! Come here, boy!" Drew hollered.

Rex and Lucky ran and jumped for several minutes before Lucky saw the treat in Drew's hand. He immediately dropped the ball and ran to get it.

Drew fed him the treat. "Good boy!" he said happily.

Rex grabbed the ball and brought it to Kyle. He liked treats, but he liked playing fetch more.

"Let's try this again. Ready, Rex?" Kyle said.

This time, Kyle threw the ball. Rex grabbed it and ran straight back. Lucky chased after him, just like Kyle had hoped.

"Come, Lucky!" Drew yelled. "Come!"

Lucky started to run past, but as soon as he saw the treat in Drew's hand he turned and raced back to his owner.

"Make a big fuss petting him, too," Kyle said. "That way he'll know you're happy with what he did."

The boys stayed at the dog park and worked with the dogs for almost an hour. Rex had a great time playing fetch with Kyle. Lucky only came straight back to Drew half the time, but it was better than the day before. The spaniel was a lot smarter than Drew realized.

But success didn't just depend on Lucky. The dog's fate depended on Drew, too.

Progress Not Perfect

Drew and Kyle decided to meet at the dog park again the following afternoon. As soon as Drew walked up, Kyle could tell he wasn't happy.

"I'm an idiot!" Drew exclaimed.

"Why?" Kyle asked. "What happened?"

Drew shook his head. "I forgot to take out the trash last night," he said.

Kyle sighed. He could guess what had happened. "So the kitchen was a mess again?" he asked.

Drew nodded. "Yep. I cleaned it up, but my parents were really upset." He hugged Lucky tightly. "I don't want to lose him. I'll have to do better tonight."

"Maybe you could write it on your hand," Kyle suggested. "Or set an alarm to remind yourself."

"That's a good idea," Drew said. "I'll try that. So what are we doing today?"

"I'll show you some more commands," Kyle said. "But then I have to work with Rex. We'll practice getting Lucky to come later."

When Drew stood up, Lucky jumped and twisted with excitement. Drew grabbed his collar. "Down, Lucky," he said firmly. "Sit down!"

"Move him to your left side," Kyle said. "That's heel. And make him sit when you're standing still."

"Heel!" Drew said. It took a few tries, but he finally managed to pull the stubborn dog around to his side. "Sit!"

Lucky barked and wagged his tail, but he didn't sit.

"Push on his back end," Kyle told him. "And when he sits, give him a treat and pet him so he knows he did what you wanted."

Drew pushed on Lucky's back end, but the dog tried to move away. He turned in several circles before finally sitting.

"Good sit!" Drew said. He quickly fed Lucky a treat.

"Now try walk and heel," Kyle said.

Lucky pranced and jumped as Drew walked him across the field. The dog didn't listen all the time, but he quickly figured out that sitting earned him a treat.

While Drew worked on getting Lucky to heel, Kyle worked with Rex. The dog paid attention and did everything Kyle asked. Kyle rewarded him with pats and praise. He had trained Rex with treats when he was a puppy, but now Rex wanted to make Kyle happy.

At least when there aren't any squirrels or poodles to distract him, Kyle thought.

Just then, Rex yanked away, pulling the leash out of Kyle's hand. He barked and charged toward a squirrel that was busy looking for food on the ground. The squirrel immediately took off for the nearest clump of trees.

"Rex, no!" Kyle shouted. He took off running after Rex.

Across the park, Lucky caught sight of the commotion and raced back toward Rex. "Lucky, stop!" Drew yelled.

The squirrel managed to escape up a tall tree, but that didn't stop the dogs. They ran around the tree, chasing each other instead.

Kyle and Drew couldn't catch them. After ten minutes, the boys collapsed on the ground.

"All that for a squirrel!" Drew exclaimed.

"Squirrels are hard to resist," Kyle said.

Before they could even catch their breath, Rex and Lucky were jumping all over them.

"It's hard to stay mad at him," Drew said. "He loves me!"

Kyle laughed as Rex licked his face. He couldn't stay mad either. Happy dogs were impossible to resist.

Kitty Crisis

I really hope Drew remembered to take out the trash last night, Kyle thought as he ran out of the house later that week. He and Rex were on their way to meet Drew at the dog park.

In just a few days, Drew's dad would decide if Lucky would be allowed to stay or have to go. Drew and his dog couldn't afford to make any more mistakes.

Kyle was in such a rush he almost didn't see Mia. She was sitting on her porch steps with her face in her hands. *Is she crying?* he wondered.

"Mia?" Kyle called as he walked over. "What's the matter?"

Mia looked up. "It's Misty. She's in big trouble. She pooped in my dad's favorite chair," she said. "And he sat on it."

Kyle bit his lip so he wouldn't laugh. It was funny, but it wasn't funny.

"Then he yelled, 'That cat is a nightmare!'" Mia wiped away a tear. "I'm really worried. What if Mom and Dad make me get rid of her?"

"They won't," Kyle said. He didn't want to miss Lucky's training session, but this was an emergency. "Maybe Misty is sick or something. Do you want to bring her to my mom's clinic? Maybe she can take a look at her and figure out what's wrong."

Mia nodded. "Good idea," she said. "Let me go get her."

It took a while for Mia to load Misty into her cat carrier. Misty was not happy about it. The clinic waiting room was empty when Kyle and Mia walked in. Only Lillian sat behind the receptionist desk.

"Does my mom have a second to look at Misty?" Kyle asked. "We think something's wrong with her."

Lillian smiled at Mia. "We've always got time for Mia's cat," she said. "Go on back to one of the exam rooms."

As they left the waiting room, Kyle realized Rex was following. His mom hadn't given the dog permission to return, but Kyle didn't want to leave Mia alone.

"Sit!" Kyle told Rex. He held up his hand. "Stay!"

Rex sat in the middle of the waiting room floor.

"Go on, Kyle," Lillian said. "I'll watch him."

Kyle's mom met them in the exam room. "What seems to be the problem with Misty today?" she asked.

"She's just crankier than usual," Mia said. "And she pooped in my dad's chair. Kyle and I thought she might be sick."

Misty hissed when Dr. Blake put her on the exam table. The vet tech held the cranky cat while Dr. Blake examined her.

"It could be that she's sick," Dr. Blake said. "Or in pain. Animals tend to act up when that's the case."

Misty tried to scratch Dr. Blake when she opened the cat's mouth. "Ah, looks like we've found our problem," she said. "Misty has an infected tooth."

"Oh, it must be hurting her!" Mia exclaimed. "I should have figured that out. I feel terrible!"

"It's not your fault, Mia," Dr. Blake said. "Animals can't tell us what's wrong. We have to guess what's going on with them and hope we get it right."

"At least now you know that Misty had a good reason for being so bad," Kyle said. "I bet your parents won't be mad anymore."

"Is she going to be okay?" Mia asked Dr. Blake.

"She'll be fine," Dr. Blake said, "but she should stay here tonight. I'll give her medicine for the pain and the infection. Then tomorrow morning I'll take out the bad tooth. She'll be back to her old self in a few days."

"Thanks, Dr. Blake," Mia said. She gave Kyle's mom a hug.

Kyle wanted to leave before his mom saw Rex in the clinic, but she followed them out to the waiting room. Rex was still sitting where Kyle had left him.

"He hasn't moved a muscle," Lillian said.

"Good dog," Dr. Blake said with a smile. She reached out and patted Rex on the head.

Yes! Kyle thought happily. He grabbed Rex's leash and hurried out before something could go wrong. He and Mia headed to the dog park, but by the time they got there, Drew and Lucky were already gone.

All Work and No Play

On Friday afternoon, Kyle got to the dog park early. He worked with Rex until Drew and Lucky arrived. Lucky sniffed the ground and pranced until Drew stopped. Then the dog sat and stared at Drew's pocket.

"I'm really sorry I wasn't here yesterday," Kyle said. "We had to take Mia's cat to the vet."

"Don't worry about it," Drew said. He gave Lucky a treat and scratched his ears. The dog looked up and thumped his tail on the ground. "We practiced on our own, and Lucky did great. Is Mia's cat okay?"

"She had a toothache," Kyle explained. "My mom fixed it this morning. How are things going? What happened with the trash?"

"I took it out!" Drew said. "Every time I look at Lucky I think *trash!* It works."

"Great!" Kyle said. "Is he still chewing?"

"Well, not exactly." Drew said with a sigh. "He's been good about using his dog toys — at least until last night. I didn't know dogs liked toilet paper! Lucky took a whole roll outside and toilet-papered the backyard!"

Kyle laughed. "Really?" he said.

Drew rolled his eyes. "There were streamers and gobs of wet paper all over the place," he said. "It took an hour to clean up, but he's *my* dog, so I did it. And my parents were impressed that I did it without having to be asked."

"That's good," Kyle said. "Do you think he's ready to show your parents that he can behave tomorrow?"

"Let's see," Drew said. He shortened Lucky's leash and started walking. Lucky followed along beside him.

"Heel," Drew said. Lucky hung back, and Drew had to drag him. "Come on, Lucky! Heel."

Rex stood up and barked.

"Sit, Rex!" Kyle commanded.

Rex sat, but he wiggled and barked. Lucky started pulling at his leash and jumping around. He managed to wrap the leash around Drew's legs.

"What's his problem?" Drew asked as he untangled his feet. "He didn't do this yesterday. If Lucky acts like this tomorrow, my parents are not going to be impressed."

"Maybe Rex and Lucky just need a break," Kyle said. "They've been training all week."

Drew frowned. "But Lucky won't get another chance with my parents if he misbehaves tomorrow," he said.

"Think about it. We get weekends off from school, right?" Kyle said. "If Lucky has fun today, maybe he'll be more willing to work tomorrow."

Drew hesitated. Then he unclipped Lucky's leash. "Do you have the ball?" he asked Kyle.

"Yep, right here," Kyle said. He pulled the ball out of his backpack and handed it to Drew. As soon as they saw it, Rex and Lucky started jumping up and down and turning in excited circles.

Drew threw the ball across the park. "Go get it!" he hollered.

Lucky reached the ball before Rex.

"Come, Lucky! Here, boy!" Drew hollered.

Lucky immediately turned and raced back to Drew. Both boys cheered happily as he dropped the ball at Drew's feet. It seemed like the training had paid off.

Kyle didn't know Drew's parents, and he didn't know how Lucky would behave tomorrow. But he knew one thing for sure — Drew and Lucky belonged together. Somehow, they had to show Drew's parents that the dog deserved to stay.

Even if he gets into trouble sometimes, Kyle thought. *Like Rex.*

Decision Day

Kyle and Mia headed over to Drew's house early Saturday morning. Rex trotted along between them.

"Aren't you worried Lucky will act up if Rex is around?" Mia asked.

"Not if I make him sit," Kyle said, grinning. "That's the one thing he does perfectly."

"I hope it's enough," Mia said.

Kyle hoped so, too. Rex's perfect sit-and-stay routine in the clinic waiting room had impressed his mom. Rex was allowed back in the clinic again, but he had to behave.

I just hope Drew's parents are as impressed, Kyle thought.

They pushed open the gate to the backyard. Drew was sitting at the picnic table and looking worried. Nearby, Lucky chased a butterfly around the yard.

"Hey, Drew!" Mia said.

"Hey, guys," Drew replied. "Thanks for coming over."

"Did your parents decide if you can keep Lucky yet?" Kyle asked.

Drew shook his head. "I was waiting for you guys to get here," he said.

"We're here!" Mia exclaimed brightly.

"Then let's get it over with," Drew said. "I'll be right back."

Kyle sat down at the picnic table, and Rex stretched out by his feet. Lucky immediately ran over to greet them. Mia petted Lucky, and he sat beside her.

Drew opened the kitchen door and stuck his head inside. "Mom! Dad!" he called. "Can you come out here for a minute?"

Mr. and Mrs. Martin stepped out onto the patio.

"What's going on?" Drew's dad asked.

"You said Lucky had to start behaving or he'd have to go back to the shelter today," Drew said.

Mr. Martin frowned. He looked confused. "But I —"

Drew kept talking. "Kyle's been helping me train Lucky," he said. "I want to show you what he's learned."

Drew's mom smiled and nudged his dad. "We'd love to see that," she said. "Wouldn't we, honey?"

Drew's dad nodded. "Of course," he said.

Drew's parents both sat down at the picnic table with Kyle and Mia. Drew clipped a leash to Lucky's collar.

"Okay," Drew said. "We're ready."

Kyle took a deep breath and crossed his fingers.

"Please be good," Mia whispered. "Please be good."

Drew started off across the yard. "Heel, Lucky," he said. Lucky hesitated as they walked past Rex, but only for a second.

"Good boy," Drew said when Lucky obeyed. He pulled a treat out of his pocket and fed it to the dog.

Kyle glanced over at Drew's parents. When Drew stopped and Lucky immediately sat down, his mom and dad exchanged a surprised look.

Drew repeated the heel-and-sit exercise two more times. Then he took the leash off and walked back toward the patio. Lucky started to follow, but another butterfly caught his attention. He took off chasing after it.

"Oh, no!" Drew's mom exclaimed as Lucky headed straight for her flower garden. The flowers would be trampled!

Drew's eyes opened wide. "Come! Come, Lucky! Come here, boy!" he shouted.

Lucky stopped and looked back at Drew. He seemed torn between catching the butterfly and listening to his owner.

Drew patted his leg. "Come on, boy!" he called encouragingly.

Kyle and Mia held their breath. They both let out sighs of relief when Lucky ran to Drew.

"Good boy!" Drew said. He knelt down and hugged the dog. Lucky wiggled with happiness and covered him with dog kisses.

"Well!" Drew's dad said, standing up, "that was quite a demonstration."

"I can't believe you taught Lucky so much," his mom added.

Drew grinned. "I had help," he said. "Kyle's a great dog trainer."

"It was mostly Drew," Kyle said. "He worked really hard with Lucky."

"And Lucky is a really smart dog," Mia added.

"How did you teach him to stay out of the trash?" Drew's dad asked.

"I didn't," Drew said. "But I've been taking it out every night so he can't get into it."

Drew's dad looked at Mrs. Martin and laughed. "I thought you were taking the trash out," he said.

"I thought you were!" Mrs. Martin said with a laugh. She looked at Drew. "Did you put my shoes away so Lucky couldn't chew them?"

"Yeah." Drew nodded and sighed. "I have to bribe Lucky with treats, and he doesn't come every time I call. He steals toilet paper rolls and chases butterflies through the garden. He's not perfect, but he's my dog and I want to keep him."

"We don't expect Lucky to be perfect," Drew's mom said. "We just want you to take some responsibility for him."

"I'm sorry, Drew," his dad said, shaking his head. "I was mad when I threatened to take Lucky back to the shelter. I didn't mean it. But I'm so proud of you for working so hard to fix the Lucky problems."

"Then I can keep him?" Drew asked.

"Of course you can," his mom said.

Kyle and Mia stayed to celebrate. The dogs played, and the kids had lemonade and cookies. Mr. Martin wanted to know all about Lucky's training. Drew answered most of his questions.

"Sounds like you're an expert, Drew," his dad said.

"I've been reading a lot," Drew explained with a smile. "It's worth it to get to keep my dog!"

An hour later, Kyle and Mia walked back to the clinic.

"Dr. Blake said Misty is ready to go home," Lillian told them when they walked in. "In fact, I think she can't wait to get out of here. She's in the back room if you want to go see her."

"Great!" Mia said. "I can't wait to have her home."

Kyle and Mia walked to the back room and one of the vet techs set the cat carrier on the table. Misty hissed and spit when she set it down.

"You don't like anyone, do you?" Kyle told the cat with a laugh.

"She likes me," Mia said.

As if to prove her point, the cranky cat purred when Mia scratched her chin through the wire door.

I guess there's a perfect pet for every person, Kyle thought. *They just have to find each other.*

AUTHOR BIO

Diana G. Gallagher lives in Florida with three dogs, eight cats, and a cranky parrot. She has written more than 90 books. When she's not writing, Gallagher likes gardening, garage sales, and spending time with her grandchildren.

ILLUSTRATOR BIO

Adriana Isabel Juárez Puglisi has been a freelance illustrator and writer for more than twenty years and loves telling stories. She currently lives in Granada, Spain, with her husband, son, daughter, two dogs, a little bird, and several fish.

Glossary

agility (uh-JIL-i-tee) — the power of moving quickly and easily

command (kuh-MAND) — to order someone to do something

confident (KON-fuh-duhnt) — having a strong belief in your own abilities

incident (IN-suh-duhnt) — something that happens; an event

irritated (IRH-uh-tay-tid) — upset or annoyed

patient (PAY-shuhnt) — someone who is receiving treatment from a doctor or other health-care provider

resist (ri-ZIST) — to refuse to accept

Discussion Questions

1. What are some other ways Kyle and Mia could have helped Drew with his pet problem? Talk about some different solutions.

2. Do you think Dr. Blake's punishment for Rex was fair? Talk about your opinion.

3. Kyle thinks there is a perfect pet for everyone. Talk about why your pet is perfect for you. If you don't have a pet, talk about what your perfect pet would be.

Writing Prompts

1. Pretend that you're Drew. Write a paragraph to your parents about why you should be able to keep Lucky.

2. Have you ever had to deal with a problem pet? Write a paragraph explaining what the problem was and how you dealt with it.

3. What do you think the best part of having a pet is? What is the hardest part? Write a paragraph about each.

Tips for Training Your Dog

Training your dog is important for many reasons. It's fun to do tricks and show off, but most importantly, it teaches your dog to listen to you. Here are some training tips to get you and your pet started.

- Be consistent — Make sure to use the same words, phrases, and commands every time. Get other family members involved too, so everyone is on the same page. Consistency is the key to success when it comes to training your pet.

- Be firm — Tell your dog what to do in a clear, calm, firm voice so he learns to recognize what you're saying as a command.

- Be affectionate — Make sure to give your dog lots of love when it does something right. You want training to be a fun experience, not a scary one. Being affectionate will make training easier and more fun for you and your pup.

- Be generous — Give your dog lots of treats when it does something right. That way, your dog will know good behavior is rewarded, and it will want to do it again.

- Be patient — Remember that training a dog takes time and work. You can't expect immediate results, so be patient with your dog during the process.

READ THE WHOLE SERIES

and learn more about
Kyle and Mia's animal adventures!

Find them all at
www.capstonepub.com